M ICHIC
knowi
regioɪ.

vascular plants distributed among 119 families. This represents about 45 percent of the roughly 2,000 native vascular plant species known in the entire state. An additional 300 introduced species occur—mostly in disturbed areas such as fields, clearings, and along roadways. Notable too are the number of rare species reported from the Keweenaw Peninsula and Isle Royale, many of which occur there and nowhere else in Michigan.

This PocketFlora Guide contains a current listing of all native and introduced vascular plants reported from the Copper Country—here defined as Houghton and Keweenaw Counties, including Isle Royale National Park. Illustrations are provided for many species. The Guide is designed for both the casual observer of plants as well as the professional botanist engaged in field studies.

Today, the natural beauty of the Keweenaw Peninsula and Isle Royale draws many during the brief summer and fall. For those willing to hike the quiet forest trails, the beaches and dunes, or the rocky mountains and ridges, the Copper Country holds a fascinating botanical wealth.

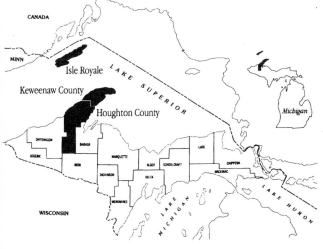

Michigan's Upper Peninsula. In this guide, the "Copper Country" (shown in black) refers to Houghton and Keweenaw Counties, including Isle Royale.

►Botanical exploration of the Copper Country

Formal interest in the plants of the region began in the 1830s when the noted state geologist Douglass Houghton made his first trips to the region. His interests went beyond the rich copper deposits he observed to include plant collecting and descriptions of the Peninsula's vegetation. Oliver Farwell, perhaps the most dedicated botanical explorer of the Keweenaw, collected thousands of plant specimens from the late 1800s until his death in 1944. More recently, Charles D. Richards completed a Ph.D. dissertation in 1952 describing the distribution of many species found on the peninsula. In 1974, James R. Wells and Paul W. Thompson published a description of the vegetation of Keweenaw County in the *Michigan Botanist;* their list included 943 species of vascular plants.

Isle Royale has also received attention. Douglass Houghton made a short visit to the island in 1840. Collections were made by A.E. Foote and others in the late 1800s. In 1909 and 1910, the influential ecologist W.S. Cooper published a series of papers on the island's vegetation. Cooper listed over 500 vascular plants, and inventoried the often overlooked moss flora. In 1930 Clair A. Brown headed a botanical survey of the island; he compiled a list of 671 flowering plants and ferns. His publication served as the standard reference for over 50 years until the publication in 1984 of a new flora of the island by Allison D. Slavick and Robert A. Janke. Their work listed approximately 700 species.

►How to use this guide

This guide is arranged by plant family and follows the family order presented in the 1991 edition of Gleason and Cronquist's *Manual of Vascular Plants of Northeastern United States and Adjacent Canada*. Their work, although without drawings, is recommended for complete descriptions and keys.

The widely available Peterson *Field Guide to Wildflowers of Northeastern and North-Central North America* has additional illustrations of many species contained in this flora (Peterson and McKenny 1968).

Within each family, genera and species are listed alphabetically. An index of family and genus names follows the species descriptions, and an index of common family names is on the inside back cover. Taxonomic nomenclature (that is, the accepted scientific plant name) follows Gleason and Cronquist, and their common names are generally used. The names of the authors who first described each species normally follow the scientific name but are omitted here for lack of space. The interested reader can find these in Gleason and Cronquist. Dr. Edward G. Voss' excellent, though incomplete two volume *Michigan Flora* (1972, 1985) was used to verify species' presence in the area. Additional, somewhat dated information was obtained from two works by Cecil Billington: *Ferns of Michigan* (1952) and *Shrubs of Michigan* (1949). Other references are listed on page 21.

SPECIES DESCRIPTIONS

The descriptions of each plant contain its two-part Latin name (genus, specific epithet) and its common name. Within some families, such as the sedges *(Carex),* common names are of limited value. With a little study and practice, use of the Latin name becomes second nature and has the added benefit of placing every plant into an orderly classification system.

A code for each species' lifeform is given:

T   tree

S   shrub

F   ferns and fern allies (such as horsetails)

G   grasses and grass-like plants (sedges, rushes)

H   other herbaceous, non-grass species ("wildflowers")

Each plant's status as either *native* to Michigan's Upper Peninsula or *introduced* from elsewhere, is noted with an *N* or *I*. Plants proposed for protection under the federal Endangered Species Act or the 1974 Endangered Species Act of Michigan (as amended) are noted with a code before the scientific name (codes listed below). Species of *Special Concern* (Michigan Natural Features Inventory 1991), although without legal protection, are also noted.

Federal

C2 listing as Endangered or Threatened may be appropriate but more information is needed

3C originally proposed for listing but species more widespread or abundant than previously thought

Michigan

E Endangered

T Threatened

X Probably extirpated from state

SC Special concern–declining or relict populations in Michigan; continued declines would lead to Threatened or Endangered listing

A brief description of each plant's typical habitat in the Copper Country is given. For many species, a description of flower and leaf characters and an illustration are included. Plants known from Isle Royale National Park are listed as *IR*. Plants known from Isle Royale but <u>not</u> the Keweenaw Peninsula are noted in the description.

▶*Traveling in the Copper Country*

Most land in the Copper Country is privately owned and property rights should be respected. Fortunately, there are a number of small parks scattered along the shoreline and inland that provide glimpses of the peninsula's major natural features. A large amount of land is owned by Champion International, much of which is open to most public uses. Visitors should stop by their office in Calumet for information. A number of nature preserves are maintained by the Michigan Nature Association, which publishes a guide to their location (the MNA can be contacted at 7981 Beard Road, Avoca, MI 48006).

Unless plants are being collected for research studies or for deposition into a herbarium, plants are best left as you find them–attached to their roots! Get into the habit of dropping to hands and knees to look closely at a plant, rather than plucking it from the ground. An inexpensive 10x hand lens will open up new worlds of detail and is an indispensable tool for successfully using the keys in other floras.

►*Major habitats of the Copper Country*

The large number of plant species found in the Copper Country is in part due to the diversity of environments present. Common plants in each of the following major habitats are described below.

- *moist forests*
- *dry forests and pine barrens*
- *wetlands*
- *lakes and ponds*
- *rocky shores*
- *mountain ridges*
- *sand dunes*
- *fields and meadows*

MOIST FORESTS

Included here are forests generally described as *northern hardwood forests* (forests of mostly deciduous trees such as sugar maple and yellow birch), *mixed forests* (a mix of deciduous trees and evergreens such as balsam fir and eastern hemlock), and *boreal forests* (predominantly conifers such as balsam fir, northern white cedar, and white spruce). Although each forest type is distinct, many of the same species occur in each.

Northern hardwood and mixed forests cover most of the heavily wooded Keweenaw Peninsula. Boreal forests are limited to low-lying areas near Lake Superior (as near Gay) but are predominant on the cool, rocky soils of Isle Royale.

• *Common plants of hardwood and mixed forests*

<u>Trees</u>

sugar maple	*Acer saccharum*
red maple	*Acer rubrum*
yellow birch	*Betula alleghaniensis*
basswood	*Tilia americana*
red oak	*Quercus rubra*
balsam fir	*Abies balsamea*

balsam fir
(*Abies balsamea*)

white pine	*Pinus strobus*
northern white cedar	*Thuja occidentalis*
eastern hemlock	*Tsuga canadensis*
big-toothed aspen	*Populus grandidentatum*
quaking aspen	*Populus tremuloides*
paper-birch	*Betula papyrifera*

<u>Shrubs</u>

thimbleberry	*Rubus parviflorus*
blueberries	*Vaccinium* spp.
bunchberry	*Cornus canadensis*

gooseberry	*Ribes* spp.
American yew	*Taxus canadensis*

<u>Ferns and clubmosses</u>

lady-fern	*Athyrium filix-femina*
bracken fern	*Pteridium aquilinum*
sensitive fern	*Onoclea sensibilis*
northern beech-fern	*Thelypteris phegopteris*
stiff clubmoss	*Lycopodium annotinum*
running pine	*Lycopodium clavatum*
northern ground-cedar	*Lycopodium complanatum*
common horsetail	*Equisetum arvense*

<u>Herbaceous plants</u>

big-leaved aster	*Aster macrophyllus*
violet	*Viola* spp.
corn-lily	*Clintonia borealis*
wild sarsaparilla	*Aralia nudicaulis*
wild lily-of-the-valley	*Maianthemum canadense*
starflower	*Trientalis borealis*
false Solomon's seal	*Smilacina racemosa*
shinleaf	*Pyrola* spp.
trout-lily	*Erythronium americanum*

• *Common plants of boreal forests*

Balsam fir and northern white cedar dominate boreal forests on the Keweenaw Peninsula. White spruce and paper birch are sometimes common. On Isle Royale, boreal forests are dominated by balsam fir, white spruce, and paper birch, with northern white cedar and quaking aspen. Common shrubs of the forest are thimbleberry *(Rubus parviflorus),* twinflower

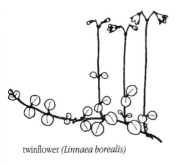

(Linnaea borealis), bunchberry *(Cornus canadensis)* and green alder *(Alnus viridis).*

twinflower *(Linnaea borealis)*

Common herbaceous species include stiff clubmoss *(Lycopodium annotinum)*, big-leaved aster *(Aster macrophyllus)*, wild sarsaparilla *(Aralia nudicaulis)*, and corn-lily *(Clintonia borealis)*.

DRY FORESTS

Dry forests are dominated by red, white, or jack pines on sandy or rocky soil. Extensive jack pine plains such as those found in Baraga County are not present in the Keweenaw. Dry forests are most common near Lake Superior on old beach ridges and dunes, and on open, rocky slopes.

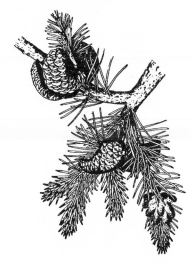

jack pine
(Pinus banksiana)

- *Common plants of dry forests*

Trees

red pine	*Pinus resinosa*
white pine	*Pinus strobus*
jack pine	*Pinus banksiana*
white spruce	*Picea glauca*
red oak	*Quercus rubra*
paper-birch	*Betula papyrifera*
showy mountain-ash	*Sorbus decora*

Shrubs

common juniper	*Juniperus communis*
buffalo berry	*Shepherdia canadensis*

bearberry	*Arctostaphylos uva-ursi*
bristly rose	*Rosa acicularis*
serviceberry	*Amelanchier* spp.
trailing arbutus	*Epigea repens*

<u>Herbaceous plants</u>

bracken fern	*Pteridium aquilinum*
wild strawberry	*Fragaria virginiana*
wintergreen	*Gaultheria procumbens*
wild lily-of-the-valley	*Maianthemum canadense*
barren strawberry	*Waldsteinia fragarioides*
big-leaved aster	*Aster macrophyllus*
bastard toadflax	*Comandra umbellata*
ticklegrass	*Agrostis gigantea*

WETLANDS

Wetlands add greatly to the diversity of the Copper Country landscape, and are home to a number of plants found nowhere else. Three major types of wetlands occur–swamps, open peatlands, and marshes. Tree-dominated swamps are the most common wetland, and are a familiar sight in low-lying areas, often presenting formidable barriers to travel on foot. Dominant trees of Copper Country swamps are northern white cedar *(Thuja occidentalis)*, tamarack *(Larix laricina)*, and black spruce *(Picea mariana)*.

Less common are open peatlands which form under anaerobic conditions (without oxygen). Plant remains accumulate faster than bacterial action can break them down, and over time an accumulation of peat many feet thick may form.

As defined by plant ecologists, Copper Country peatlands are *fens* rather than true *bogs*. Fens are waterlogged wetlands in contact with underlying groundwater and nutrient-enriched by runoff from their surroundings. Conversely, the surface of a bog is elevated *above* the surrounding water level by the accumulation of peat. Minerals come from rain and snow—little better than distilled water as a nutrient source. These

differences account for a greater diversity of species in fens, while bogs are suitable for only a limited number of species adapted to extremely acidic, nutrient poor conditions. In both types of peatlands, mosses such as sphagnum may form a nearly continuous, hummocky carpet.

sphagnum moss
(Sphagnum centrale)

• *Common plants of swamps and fens*

Shrubs

speckled alder	*Alnus incana*
bog-rosemary	*Andromeda glaucophylla*
leatherleaf	*Chamaedaphne calyculata*
Labrador-tea	*Ledum groenlandicum*
swamp-laurel	*Kalmia polifolia*
sweet gale	*Myrica gale*
red osier-dogwood	*Cornus sericea*
bunchberry	*Cornus canadensis*
shining willow	*Salix lucida*
red maple	*Acer rubrum*
cranberry	*Vaccinium macrocarpon*
small cranberry	*Vaccinium oxycoccos*
common mountain-holly	*Nemopanthus mucronata*
meadowsweet	*Spiraea alba*

Grasses and grass-like plants

blue-joint	*Calamagrostis canadensis*
fowl-mannagrass	*Glyceria striata*
sedge	*Carex oligosperma*
slender sedge	*Carex lasiocarpa*

sedge	*Carex pauciflora*
sedge	*Carex livida*
sedge	*Carex limosa*
sedge	*Carex disperma*
sedge	*Carex interior*
sedge	*Carex leptalea*
sedge	*Carex paupercula*
cotton-grass	*Eriophorum* spp.
beak-rush	*Rhynchospora alba*

Other herbaceous plants

water horsetail	*Equisetum fluviatile*
dwarf scouring rush	*Equisetum scirpoides*
buckbean	*Menyanthes trifoliata*
false Solomon's seal	*Smilacina trifolia*
marsh-marigold	*Caltha palustris*
yellow lady-slipper	*Cypripedium calceolus*
tall northern bog-orchid	*Habenaria hyperborea*
rose pogonia	*Pogonia ophioglossoides*
northern blue flag	*Iris versicolor*
pitcher-plant	*Sarracenia purpurea*
round-leaved sundew	*Drosera rotundifolia*

The final wetland type, marsh, is characterized by emergent plants such as cat-tail *(Typha latifolia),* wool-grass *(Scirpus cyperinus),* hardstem-bulrush *(Scirpus acutus),* and soft rush

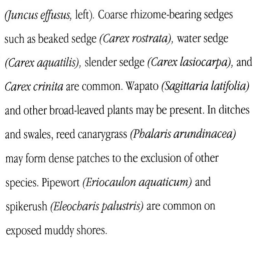

(Juncus effusus, left). Coarse rhizome-bearing sedges such as beaked sedge *(Carex rostrata),* water sedge *(Carex aquatilis),* slender sedge *(Carex lasiocarpa),* and *Carex crinita* are common. Wapato *(Sagittaria latifolia)* and other broad-leaved plants may be present. In ditches and swales, reed canarygrass *(Phalaris arundinacea)* may form dense patches to the exclusion of other species. Pipewort *(Eriocaulon aquaticum)* and spikerush *(Eleocharis palustris)* are common on exposed muddy shores.

LAKES & PONDS

Lakes and ponds dot the Copper Country landscape–
Keweenaw County has nearly 100 named lakes and ponds; Isle
Royale has over 80. Listed below are true aquatic plants–plants
either floating on the water surface (such as duckweed and the
bladderworts) or rooted in bottom sediments (pondweeds,
water lily). Common emergent species, such as bulrushes and
cattails, are listed under wetlands.

- *Common aquatic plants of lakes and ponds*

pondweeds   *Potamogeton amplifolius*

                                         P. epihydrus

                                         P.gramineus

                                         P. natans

                                         P. praelongus (left), others

water-lily   *Nuphar variegata*

water-shield   *Brasenia schreberi*

white water-lily   *Nymphaea odorata*

water-celery   *Vallisneria americana*

duckweed   *Lemna minor*

common waterweed   *Elodea canadensis*

northern water-nymph   *Najas flexilis*

common bladderwort   *Utricularia vulgaris*

white water-crowfoot   *Ranunculus longirostris*

ROCKY SHORES

The Keweenaw Peninsula and Isle Royale are ringed by the
rugged, rocky shoreline of Lake Superior. Here, an interesting
assortment of stunted trees, shrubs and herbaceous species
find their niche amongst rock crevices. Plants occupying this
habitat are listed on page 13.

Shrubs

green alder	*Alnus viridis*
showy mountain-ash	*Sorbus decora*
bearberry	*Arctostaphylos uva-ursi*
sweet gale	*Myrica gale*
buffalo berry	*Shepherdia canadensis*
common juniper	*Juniperus communis*
thimbleberry	*Rubus parviflorus*
bush-honeysuckle	*Diervilla lonicera*
dwarf raspberry	*Rubus pubescens*
shrubby cinquefoil	*Potentilla fruticosa*
prickly rose	*Rosa acicularis*

Herbaceous plants

poverty-oatgrass	*Danthonia spicata*
harebell	*Campanula rotundifolia*
beach pea	*Lathyrus maritimus*
tall wormwood	*Artemisia campestris*
mountain white cinquefoil	*Potentilla tridentata*
tall cinquefoil	*Potentilla arguta*
goldenrod	*Solidago simplex*
Canada hawkweed	*Hieracium kalmii*
wild strawberry	*Fragaria virginiana*
bird's-eye primrose	*Primula mistassinica*
marsh violet	*Viola nephrophylla*
common yarrow	*Achillea millefolium*
white paintbrush	*Castilleja septentrionalis*
	(threatened in Michigan)

MOUNTAIN RIDGES

Exposed mountain ridges such as atop Brockway Mountain, receive the full force of winds off Lake Superior. The resulting effects on plant growth are striking. Typically, widely scattered, stunted trees and shrubs occur as "islands", with a short carpet of plants between the patches of taller vegetation.

• *Plants of mountain ridges*

Trees

quaking aspen	*Populus tremuloides*
red maple	*Acer rubrum*
red oak	*Quercus rubra*
balsam fir	*Abies balsamea*
northern white cedar	*Thuja occidentalis*
white spruce	*Picea glauca*

Shrubs

common juniper	*Juniperus communis*
serviceberry	*Amelanchier* spp.
thimbleberry	*Rubus parviflorus*
buffalo berry	*Shepherdia canadensis*
snowberry	*Symphoricarpos albus*
bearberry	*Arctostaphylos uva-ursi*
horizontal juniper	*Juniperus horizontalis*
prickly rose	*Rosa acicularis*

Herbaceous plants

three-toothed cinquefoil	*Potentilla tridentata*
wild strawberry	*Fragaria virginiana*
goldenrod	*Solidago simplex*
showy goldenrod	*Solidago speciosa*
Canada hawkweed	*Hieracium kalmii*
harebell	*Campanula rotundifolia*
large-leaved aster	*Aster macrophyllus*
hairgrass	*Deschampsia flexuosa*
poverty-oatgrass	*Danthonia spicata*

| rusty cliff-fern | *Woodsia ilvensis* |
| rock spikemoss | *Selaginella rupestris* |

SAND DUNES

The Keweenaw is home to several sand dune fields, most notably along Great Sand Bay, where dunes 100 feet high have formed. Moving away from the lake, the dunes change from open shifting sands, to dunes stabilized by patches of beach grass *(Ammophila breviligulata),* to dry woods of red pine and red oak. Gray-green reindeer lichens *(Cladonia* spp.) are conspicuous. Wetlands are sometimes found in the hollows between dune ridges. Near Rice Lake, an interesting series of glacial beach lines form a repeating linear pattern: low sandy ridges supporting jack pine are interspersed with wet swales dominated by sphagnum and *Carex oligosperma.*

• *Plants of sand dunes*

Trees

red pine	*Pinus resinosa*
jack pine	*Pinus banksiana*
red oak	*Quercus rubra*

Shrubs

common juniper	*Juniperus communis*
lowbush blueberry	*Vaccinium angustifolium*
sand-cherry	*Prunus pumila*
bearberry	*Arctostaphylos uva-ursi*
false heather	*Hudsonia tomentosa*

Grasses and other herbaceous plants

beach-grass	*Ammophila breviligulata*
beach pea	*Lathyrus maritimus*
tall wormwood	*Artemisia campestris*
sand cress	*Arabis lyrata*
wild strawberry	*Fragaria virginiana*
jointweed	*Polygonella articulata*
sedge	*Carex pensylvanica*

FIELDS & MEADOWS

Openings in the once nearly continuous forest cover of the Copper Country reflect the presence of humans. The history of the peninsula includes a tremendous copper mining boom in the mid-1800s. Large tracts of level forest land were cleared for agriculture and vast amounts of timber were harvested for industrial and residential needs. Today, the forest cover has returned in most areas. The remaining open fields are home to a large number of non-native species either intentionally introduced such as alfalfa *(Medicago sativa)* or unwelcome invaders such as the knapweeds *(Centaurea* spp.) and hawkweeds *(Hieracium)*. One casualty not soon to be replaced are the giant white pines that towered above many forests prior to the mining period. The Estivant Pines south of Copper Harbor are an outstanding example of a remnant white pine forest.

- *Common plants of fields and meadows*

Grasses

orchard-grass	*Dactylis glomerata*
timothy	*Phleum pratense*
Kentucky bluegrass	*Poa pratensis*
Canada bluegrass	*Poa compressa*
redtop	*Agrostis gigantea*
ticklegrass	*Agrostis hyemalis*
quack-grass	*Elytrigea repens*
smooth brome	*Bromus inermis*

Other plants

common goldenrod	*Solidago canadense*
smooth goldenrod	*Solidago gigantea*
common buttercup	*Ranunculus acris*
orange hawkweed	*Hieracium aurantiacum*
yellow hawkweed	*Hieracium kalmii*
ox-eye daisy	*Chrysanthemum leucanthemum*

common St. John's-wort	*Hypericum perforatum*
spotted joe-pye weed	*Eupatorium maculatum*
common tansy	*Tanacetum vulgare*
queen Anne's lace	*Daucus carota*
fireweed	*Epilobium angustifolium*
common milkweed	*Asclepias syriaca*
common dandelion	*Taraxacum officinale*
sulfur cinquefoil	*Potentilla recta*
red clover	*Trifolium pratense*
bouncing bet	*Saponaria officinalis*
bracken fern	*Pteridium aquilinum*
black-eyed Susan	*Rudbeckia hirta*
common yarrow	*Achillea millefolium*
wild strawberry	*Fragaria virginiana*

▶ Rare plants of the Copper Country

The Keweenaw Peninsula and Isle Royale support a surprising number of rare plants. Most of these species are considered rare because they are *disjunct*, or separated by a large distance from their main geographic range in the mountains of western North America (see Marquis and Voss 1981). Although disjunct, some of these species are locally common in the Keweenaw area. Thimbleberry *(Rubus parviflorus)* and trail-plant *(Adenocaulon bicolor)* are good examples.

A second group of uncommon plants are termed *peripheral* species. They are widely distributed in arctic regions to the north, but occur on the Keweenaw Peninsula or Isle Royale at the extreme southern edge of their range (Given and Soper 1981).

The final group includes species restricted to uncommon habitats and species found naturally in only small numbers or at widely scattered locales. Species declines are also brought about by habitat loss.

All plants known to have special status are indicated in this guide. More information on these species is available by contacting the Michigan Natural Features Inventory, Mason Building, P.O. Box 30028, Lansing, MI 48909. As of 1996, there were no species federally listed as Endangered or Threatened on the Keweenaw Peninsula or Isle Royale.

• *Western disjunct species and their status**

<u>Keweenaw Peninsula and Isle Royale</u>

–	rock cress	*Arabis holboellii*
T	small blue-eyed Mary	*Collinsia parviflora*
SC	black hawthorn	*Crataegus douglasii*
–	western fescue	*Festuca occidentalis*
–	w. rattlesnake-plantain	*Goodyera oblongifolia*
–	tapering sweet cicely	*Osmorhiza chilensis*
–	smartweed	*Polygonum douglasii*
–	thimbleberry	*Rubus parviflorus*

<u>Keweenaw Peninsula only</u>

–	trail-plant	*Adenocaulon bicolor*
T	heart-leaved arnica	*Arnica cordifolia* (=*"A. whitneyi"*)
X	bluebunch wheatgrass	*Elytrigea spicata* (=*Agropyron spicatum;* may be extirpated from Michigan)
C2/E	Keweenaw rock-rose	*Chamaerhodos erecta* (=*C. nuttallii* var. *keweenawensis*)
T	redstem ceanothus	*Ceanothus sanguineus*
–	awned melic grass	*Melica smithii*
–	musky monkey-flower	*Mimulus moschatus*
–	northern holly-fern	*Polystichum lonchitis*
T	pine-drops	*Pterospora andromeda*
–	mountain-bilberry	*Vaccinium membranaceum*

* Status codes: *E* (endangered in Michigan), *T* (threatened in Michigan), *X* (extirpated from state), *SC* (special concern), *C2* (federal listing may be warranted but more information needed), *3C* (species once proposed for Federal listing but more abundant than previously believed).

–	tall bilberry	*Vaccinium ovalifolium*
SC	sedge	*Carex praegracilis*
		(Isle Royale only)
T	sandwort	*Arenaria macrophylla*
T	parsley-fern	*Cryptogramma crispa*
T	devil's club	*Oplopanax horridus*
T	Canby's bluegrass	*Poa canbyi*

• *Peripheral species*

T	braya	*Braya humilis*
–	sedge	*Carex capillaris*
T	northeastern paintbrush	*Castilleja septentrionalis*
T	draba	*Draba arabisans*
T	draba	*Draba incana*
		(Isle Royale only)
–	fragrant wood-fern	*Dryopteris fragrans*
T	black crowberry	*Empetrum nigrum*
–	eyebright	*Euphrasia hudsoniana*
		(Isle Royale only)
T	rush	*Juncus stygius*
		(Isle Royale only)
SC	fir-clubmoss	*Lycopodium selago*
T	water-lily	*Nymphaea tetragona*
SC	violet butterwort	*Pinguicula vulgaris*
T	alpine bluegrass	*Poa alpina*
–	bluegrass	*Poa glauca*
T	alpine bistort	*Polygonum viviparum*
–	Mistassini primrose	*Primula mistassinica*
T	pearlwort	*Sagina nodosa*
T	lime-crusted saxifrage	*Saxifraga tricuspidata*
		(Isle Royale only)
–	tufted bulrush	*Scirpus cespitosus*
–	northern spikemoss	*Selaginella selaginoides*
SC	reclining goldenrod	*Solidago decumbens*

T	false asphodel	*Tofieldia pusilla*
		(Isle Royale only)
SC	trisetum	*Trisetum spicatum*
T	bog-bilberry	*Vaccinium uliginosum*
X	lingonberry	*Vaccinium vitis-idaea*

Keweenaw rock-rose *(Chamaerhodos erecta)*. In Michigan, this member of the Rose Family is known only from Brockway Mountain on the Keweenaw Peninsula.

▶*References*

Billington, Cecil. 1949. *Shrubs of Michigan* (second . edition).Cranbrook Institute of Science Bulletin 20. Bloomfield Hills, Michigan. 339 pp.

Billington, Cecil. 1952. *Ferns of Michigan.* Cranbrook Institute of Science Bulletin 32. Bloomfield Hills, Michigan. 239 pp.

Case, Frederick W. Jr., and Paul M. Catling. 1983. *The genus* Spiranthes *in Michigan.* Michigan Botanist 22:79-92.

Given, D.R., and J.H. Soper. 1981. *The arctic-alpine element of the vascular flora at Lake Superior.* National Museum of Natural Sciences. Ottawa, Canada. Publications in Botany No. 10. 70 pp.

Gleason, Henry A., and Arthur Cronquist. 1991. *Manual of Vascular Plants of Northeastern United States and Adjacent Canada.* The New York Botanical Garden. Bronx, New York.

Marquis, Robert J., and Edward G. Voss. 1981. *Distributions of some western North American plants disjunct in the Great Lakes region.* Michigan Botanist 20:53-82.

Peterson, Roger T., and Margaret McKenny. 1968. *A Field Guide to Wildflowers of Northeastern and North-Central North America.* Houghton Mifflin Company, Boston.

Richards, Charles D. 1952. *Phytogeographic studies in northern Michigan.* Ph.D. dissertation; University of Michigan, Ann Arbor.

Slavick, Alison D., and Robert A. Janke. 1993. *The Vascular Flora of Isle Royale National Park* (third ed.). Isle Royale Natural History Association, Houghton, Michigan. 50 pp.

Voss, Edward G. 1972. *Michigan Flora Part 1: Gymnosperms and Monocots.* Cranbrook Institute of Science Bulletin 55 and Univ. of Michigan Herbarium. 488 pp.

Voss, Edward G. 1985. *Michigan Flora Part 2: Dicots (Saururaceae–Cornaceae).* Cranbrook Institute of Science Bulletin 59 and Univ. of Michigan Herbarium. 724 pp.

Wells, James R., and Paul W. Thompson. 1974. *Vegetation and flora of Keweenaw County, Michigan.* Michigan Botanist 13:107-151.

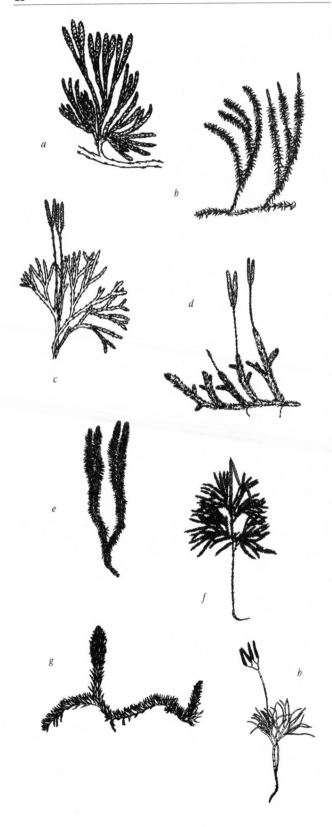

(a) Lycopodium alpinum, (b) L. annotinum, (c) L. complanatum, (d) L. clavatum, (e) L. lucidulum, (f) L. selago, (g) L. inundatum, (b) L. tristachyum

Status codes: *E* (endangered in Michigan), *T* (threatened in Michigan), *X* (extirpated from state), *SC* (special concern), *C2* (federal listing may be warranted but more information needed), *3C* (species once proposed for Federal listing but more abundant than previously believed).

►*Lycopodiaceae*   Clubmoss Family

Lycopodium alpinum   **alpine clubmoss**   F   N
❋   rocky openings; conifer forests

Lycopodium annotinum   **stiff clubmoss**   F   N   IR
❋   acidic soil under conifers

Lycopodium clavatum   **running pine**   F   N   IR
❋   mixed or jack pine woods; rocky places

Lycopodium complanatum   **northern ground-cedar**   F   N   IR
❋   mixed and conifer forests

Lycopodium digitatum   **southern ground-cedar**   F   N
dry woods and clearings

Lycopodium inundatum   **bog-clubmoss**   F   N   IR
❋   sphagnum peatlands

Lycopodium lucidulum   **shining clubmoss**   F   N   IR
❋   moist hardwood and conifer forests; leaves shiny

Lycopodium obscurum   **ground-pine**   F   N   IR
mixed and conifer forests

SC **Lycopodium selago**   **fir-clubmoss**   F   N   IR
❋   exposed rock ridges and shores, often in patches of sphagnum; more common northward

Lycopodium tristachyum   **wiry ground-cedar**   F   N   IR
❋   dry, open sandy woods and clearings

►*Selaginellaceae*   Selaginella Family

Selaginella rupestris   **rock spikemoss**   F   N   IR
rocky ridges and rock shores along Lake Superior

Selaginella selaginoides   **northern spikemoss**   F   N   IR
❋   moist places in rocks; mostly along Lake Superior shoreline

►*Isoetaceae*   Quillwort Family

Isoetes echinospora   **spiny-spored quillwort**   F   N   IR
❋   plants usually submersed in shallow water

Isoetes lacustris   **deep-water quillwort**   F   N   IR
plants submersed in shallow water or along drying shores

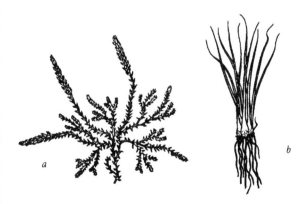

(a) Selaginella selaginoides, (b) Isoetes echinospora

Lifeform codes: *T* (tree), *S* (shrub), *H* (herbaceous flowering plants), *G* (grasses and grass-like plants), *F* (ferns and fern-allies). Origin codes: *N* (native to Upper Peninsula), *I* (introduced species). Present on Isle Royale: *IR* (present), *blank* (absent). ❋ indicates an illustrated species.

▶*Equisetaceae*   Horsetail Family

Equisetum arvense   **common horsetail**   F   N   IR
- ❋   wide variety of mostly moist habitats; sometimes weedy along roadsides

Equisetum fluviatile   **water-horsetail**   F   N   IR
- ❋   shallow water, marshes, wet places in peatlands

Equisetum byemale   **common scouring rush**   F   N   IR
- ❋   moist places and streambanks; usually in forests

Equisetum laevigatum   **smooth scouring rush**   F   N
      moist areas and streambanks; marshes

Equisetum palustre   **marsh-horsetail**   F   N   IR
- ❋   swamps, streambanks, marshes and lakeshores

Equisetum pratense   **meadow-horsetail**   F   N   IR
      moist forests and meadows; streambanks

Equisetum scirpoides   **dwarf scouring rush**   F   N   IR
- ❋   moist forests, often along wetland margins; plants slender and less than one foot tall

Equisetum sylvaticum   **woodland-horsetail**   F   N   IR
- ❋   wet woods and swamps; streambanks

X   **Equisetum telmateia**   **giant horsetail**   F   N
      possibly extinct from Michigan; plants robust, to 6 feet tall

Equisetum variegatum   **variegated scouring rush**   F   N   IR
- ❋   shorelines; moist sandy areas; streambanks

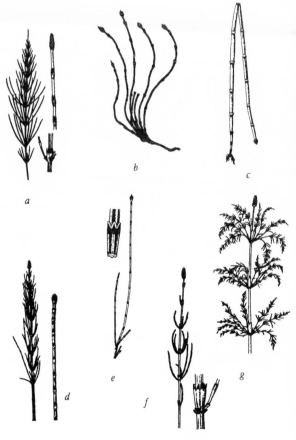

(a) Equisetum arvense, (b) E. scirpoides, (c) E. byemale, (d) E. fluviatile,
(e) E. variegatum , (f) E. palustre, (g) E. sylvaticum.

▶ *Ophioglossaceae*   Adder's tongue Family

Botrychium dissectum   **lace-frond grape-fern**   F   N
    dry open forests and meadows

Botrychium lanceolatum   **lance-leaved g.-fern**   F   N   IR
    range of habitats–dry to moist

Botrychium lunaria   **moonwort**   F   N   IR
    ✸   rocky or gravelly openings and meadows

Botrychium matricariaefolium   **daisy-leaved g.-f.**   F   N   IR
    moist woods

Botrychium multifidum   **leathery grape-fern**   F   N   IR
    ✸   dry woods and rocky openings

Botrychium simplex   **little grape-fern**   F   N   IR
    wetland margins; moist meadows

Botrychium virginianum   **rattlesnake-fern**   F   N   IR
    ✸   mostly in moist forests; most common moonwort

Ophioglossum vulgatum   **adder's-tongue**   F   N
    moist woods and meadows; plants small, difficult to find

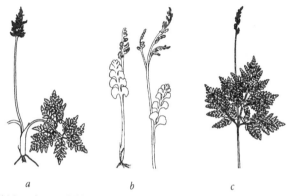

     a   *b*   *c*

(a) Botrychium multifidum, (b) B. lunaria, (c) B. virginianum

▶ *Osmundaceae*   Royal Fern Family

Osmunda cinnamonea   **cinnamon-fern**   F   N   IR
    ✸   moist, shady forests; wetland margins

Osmunda claytoniana   **interrupted fern**   F   N   IR
    ✸   low places in moist forests; swamps

Osmunda regalis   **royal fern**   F   N   IR
    ✸   low places in forests; swamps

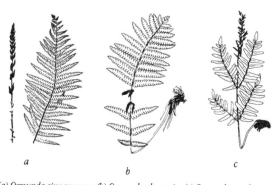

     a   *b*   *c*

(a) Osmunda cinnamonea, (b) Osmunda claytonia, (c) Osmunda regalis

---

►*Polypodiaceae*　　　Polypody Family

Polypodium virginianum　　**common polypody**　　F　N　IR
✱　　rocky shoreline of Lake Superior; inland rocky openings

►*Dennstaedtiaceae*　　　Bracken Family

Dennstaedtia punctilobula　**hay-scented fern**　　F　N
　　　in Michigan known only from rocky places in Keweenaw
　　　County; plant of eastern Canada and US

Pteridium aquilinum　　　**bracken fern**　　F　N　IR
✱　　common rhizomatous fern of young forests and sterile sandy
　　　soils; scattered in mature forests

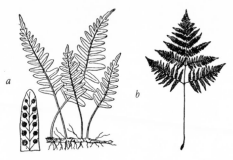

(a) Polypodium virginianum, (b) Pteridium aquilinum

►*Adiantaceae*　　　Maidenhair Fern Family

　Adiantum pedatum　　　　**maidenhair fern**　　F　N
　　✱　　rich woods; sometimes on rock

T　**Cryptogramma crispa**　　**parsley-fern**　　　F　N　IR
　　　　Isle Royale; rock shorelines and openings

SC　**Cryptogramma stelleri**　　**slender rock-brake**　F　N　IR
　　✱　　rock shores and openings

T　**Pellaea atropurpurea**　　**purple cliff-brake**　　F　N
　　　　rocks and cliffs; Brockway Mountain; plants remain green
　　　　through winter

　Pellaea glabella　　　　**smooth cliff-brake**　　F　N
　　✱　　rock crevices

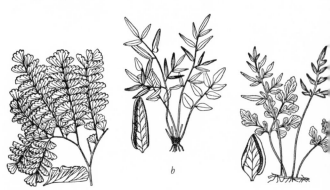

(a) Adiantum pedatum, (b) Pellaea glabella, (c) Cryptogramma stelleri

►*Aspleniaceae*   Spleenwort Family

X **Asplenium montanum**   **mountain spleenwort** F N
    in Michigan, once known from rocky places in the
    Keweenaw; may now be extinct in state

T **Asplenium rhizophyllum**   **walking fern**   F N
    ❀ moist shaded, mossy rocks; rare in Michigan; also known as
    Camptosorus rhizophyllum

   Asplenium ruta-muraria   **wall-rue**   F N
    rocky cliffs, ridges and woods

   Asplenium trichomanes   **maidenhair spleenwort** F N IR
    ❀ usually on shaded rocks

(a) Asplenium rhizophyllum, (b) Asplenium trichomanes.

T **Asplenium viride**   **green spleenwort**   F N
    shaded, usually calcium-rich rocks; rare in Michigan

   Athyrium filix-femina   **lady-fern**   F N IR
    ❀ common fern of moist forests and hummocks in swamps

   Cystopteris bulbifera   **bulblet bladder-fern** F N
    moist forests and ravines; wet rocky places

   Cystopteris fragilis   **brittle bladder-fern** F N IR
    ❀ Lake Superior rocky shore; open, rocky woods

   Dryopteris carthusiana   **toothed wood-fern** F N IR
    moist mixed or conifer forests; swamps

   Dryopteris cristata   **crested wood-fern** F N IR
    ❀ moist forests and swamps; sometimes in open peatlands

(a) Athyrium filix-femina, (b) Cystopteris fragilis, (c) Dryopteris cristata

SC **Dryopteris expansa**   **northern wood-fern** F N IR
    mixed and conifer forests

T **Dryopteris filix-mas**   **male fern**   F N
    shady rocky places, moist cliff bases; moist forests and
    streambanks; rare in Michigan

Lifeform codes: *T* (tree), *S* (shrub), *H* (herbaceous flowering plants), *G* (grasses and grass-like plants, *F* (ferns and fern-allies). Origin codes: *N* (native to Upper Peninsula), *I* (introduced species). Present on Isle Royale: *IR* (present), *blank* (absent). ❀ indicates an illustrated species.

Dryopteris fragrans **fragrant wood-fern** F N IR
rocks and crevices; talus slopes

Dryopteris goldiana **Goldie's wood-fern** F N
rich woods

Dryopteris intermedia **fancy wood-fern** F N IR
❀ mixed hardwood and conifer forests

Dryopteris marginalis **marginal wood-fern** F N IR
mixed and conifer forests; rock ledges

Gymnocarpium dryopteris **oak-fern** F N IR
❀ moist or wet deciduous and conifer forests

Gymnocarpium robertianum **limestone oak-fern** F N
usually on calcium-rich rocks

Polystichum acrostichoides **Christmas-fern** F N
woods and shaded rocky slopes

Polystichum braunii **Braun's holly-fern** F N
rocky woods and slopes

Polystichum lonchitis **northern holly-fern** F N
❀ shaded rocks and talus

Thelypteris hexagonoptera **southern beech-fern** F N
dry oak woods; uncommon in Keweenaw

Thelypteris palustris **marsh-fern** F N IR
peatlands and forested ravines

Thelypteris phegopteris **northern beech-fern** F N IR
❀ moist woods and swamps

T *Woodsia alpina* **alpine cliff-fern** F N
on moist rocks; in Michigan, known only from Keweenaw County

Woodsia ilvensis **rusty cliff-fern** F N IR
❀ Lake Superior rocky shores; rocky ridges

T *Woodsia obtusa* **blunt cliff-fern** F N
rocky slopes and talus; in Michigan, known only from Keweenaw County

Woodsia oregana **western cliff-fern** F N
rock crevices; Brockway Mountain

(a) Gymnocarpium dryopteris, (b) Polystichum lonchitis, (c) Dryopteris intermedia, (d) Thelypteris phegopteris, (e) Woodsia ilvensis

Status codes: *E* (endangered in Michigan), *T* (threatened in Michigan), *X* (extirpated from state), *SC* (special concern), *C2* (federal listing may be warranted but more information needed), *3C* (species once proposed for Federal listing but more abundant than previously believed).

►*Onocleaceae*   Sensitive Fern Family

Matteuccia struthiopteris   **ostrich-fern**   F   N   IR
- ✿   shady places in moist woods; especially in ravines and seepy areas

Onoclea sensibilis   **sensitive fern**   F   N   IR
- ✿   moist swales and ravines in forests

(a) Matteuccia struthiopteris, (b) Onoclea sensibilis

►*Taxaceae*   Yew Family

Taxus canadensis   **American yew**   S   N   IR
- ✿   rich woods and ravines; cedar swamps; a favored deer browse

Taxus canadensis

►*Pinaceae*   Pine Family

Abies balsamea   **balsam fir**   T   N   IR
- ✿   mixed forests; cedar swamps; common

Larix laricina   **tamarack**   T   N   IR
- ✿   wet places, often with spruce; leaves deciduous in fall

Picea glauca   **white spruce**   T   N   IR
- ✿   conifer swamps, mixed forests, streambanks, wooded dunes, shorelines; young branches without hairs

(a) Abies balsamea, (b) Larix laricina

Lifeform codes: *T* (tree), *S* (shrub), *H* (herbaceous flowering plants), *G* (grasses and grass-like plants), *F* (ferns and fern-allies). Origin codes: *N* (native to Upper Peninsula), *I* (introduced species). Present on Isle Royale: *IR* (present), *blank* (absent). ✿ indicates an illustrated species.

Picea mariana   **black spruce**   T   N   IR

❀   most common in swamps with cedar; more common northward in spruce-fir forest; young branches with fine hairs

(a) Picea glauca, (b) Picea mariana

Pinus banksiana   **jack pine**   T   N   IR

❀   scrubby tree of dry, sandy soil or rocky shores; sometimes also on peatland hummocks

Pinus resinosa   **red pine**   T   N   IR

❀   tall tree of sandy and rocky soils; wooded dunes and ridges; often with jack pine and oaks;

Pinus strobus   **white pine**   T   N   IR

❀   mixed forests of maple, yellow birch, hemlock; also in drier woods and rock; or sometimes cedar swamps

Tsuga canadensis   **eastern hemlock**   T   N

❀   moist forests with maple, yellow birch and white pine; conifer swamps

(a) Pinus banksiana, (b) Pinus resinosa, (c) Pinus strobus, (d) Tsuga canadensis

---

Status codes: *E* (endangered in Michigan), ·*T* (threatened in Michigan), *X* (extirpated from state), *SC* (special concern), *C2* (federal listing may be warranted but more information needed), *3C* (species once proposed for Federal listing but more abundant than previously believed).

►*Cupressaceae*   Cypress Family

Juniperus communis   **common juniper**   S   N   IR
        common on wooded dunes near Lake Superior; also on rock
        ridges and shores; hummocks in swamps

Juniperus horizontalis   **creeping juniper**   S   N   IR
        rock ridges and shores

Thuja occidentalis   **northern white cedar**   T   N   IR
   ❀ major tree of swamps; present in moist mixed woods;
        streambanks; important deer browse

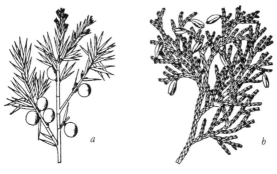

(a) Juniperus communis, (b) Thuja occidentalis

►*Aristolochiaceae*   Birthwort Family

Asarum canadense   **wild-ginger**   H   N   IR
   ❀ moist, rich mostly deciduous forests; flowers red-brown, below
        leaves and often near ground; edible rhizomes once used for
        ginger

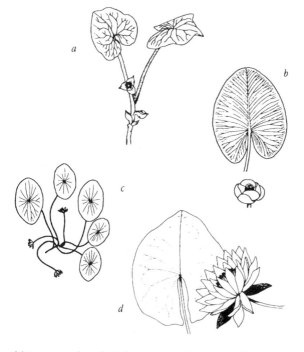

(a) Asarum canadense, (b) Nuphar variegata, (c) Brasenia schreberi,
(d) Nymphaea odorata

Lifeform codes: *T* (tree), *S* (shrub), *H* (herbaceous flowering plants), *G* (grasses and grass-like
plants, *F* (ferns and fern-allies). Origin codes: *N* (native to Upper Peninsula), *I* (introduced species).
Present on Isle Royale: *IR* (present), *blank* (absent). ❀ indicates an illustrated species.

▶ *Nymphaeaceae* Water-Lily Family

Brasenia schreberi **water-shield** H N IR
* lakes and ponds; floating leaves 2-4 inches across; stem attached to center of leaf underside, slimy; flower small and dull-purple

Nuphar variegata **water-lily** H N IR
* lakes and ponds, sometimes slow streams; flowers 3 inches wide, sepals yellow, reddish inside near base

Nymphaea odorata **white water-lily** H N IR
* ponds and lake bays; flowers white and fragrant

T **Nymphaea tetragona** **water-lily** H N IR
in Michigan, known only from single stream on Isle Royale; more common northward

▶ *Ceratophyllaceae* Hornwort Family

Ceratophyllum echinatum **coontail** H N IR
submersed plants of softwater (acidic) ponds and lakes

▶ *Ranunculaceae* Buttercup Family

Actaea alba **white baneberry** H N IR
* rich hardwood or mixed forests; fruit white with a purple spot

Actaea rubra **red baneberry** H N IR
moist forests; sometimes swamps; fruit a cluster of shiny red berries; poisonous

Anemone canadensis **Canadian anemone** H N IR
* moist openings and streambanks; may form large colonies; flowers with white sepals and gold stamens

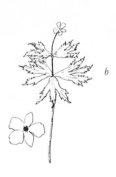

(a) Actaea alba, (b) Anenome canadensis

Anemone multifida **cut-leaved anemone** H N IR
rock ridges and shores on Isle Royale

Anemone quinquefolia **wood-anemone** H N IR
mixed woods and swamps; single flowers with 5 white sepals and no petals

Anemone virginiana **tall-anemone** H N IR
mostly drier woods and meadows; but also occasional in swamps

Aquilegia canadensis **Canada-columbine** H N IR
forest openings and borders; rock ridges; flowers usually red with yellow centers

Aquilegia vulgaris   **European columbine**   H   I

> escape from cultivation; flowers various colors (purple, white, yellow or pink)

Caltha palustris   **marsh-marigold**   H   N   IR

> ❀   open swamps and marshes; common yellow-gold shiny flowered plant of Keweenaw wetlands in early spring

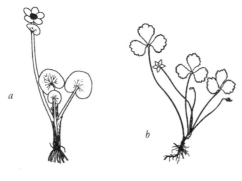

(a) Caltha palustris, (b) Coptis trifolia

SC   *Clematis occidentalis*   **clematis, woodbine**   H   N   IR

> dry, rocky woods and clearings

Clematis virginiana   **virgin's bower**   S   N   IR

> vine of moist woods and streambanks; wetland margins; vine with white flowers, pistils lengthen into plumes

Coptis trifolia   **goldthread**   H   N   IR

> ❀   usually in cedar swamps on hummocks; flowers solitary, white on leafless stalk; named for golden color of creeping rhizome

Hepatica americana   **round-lobed hepatica**   H   N   IR

> moist to dry forests; three-lobed leaves persisting over winter

Ranunculus abortivus   **small-flowered buttercup**   H   N   IR

> ❀   mixed forests; common

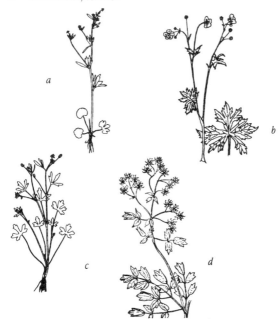

(a) Ranunculus abortivus, (b) Ranunculus acris, (c) Ranunculus sceleratus,
(d) Thalictrum dasycarpum

Lifeform codes: *T* (tree), *S* (shrub), *H* (herbaceous flowering plants), *G* (grasses and grass-like plants), *F* (ferns and fern-allies). Origin codes: *N* (native to Upper Peninsula), *I* (introduced species). Present on Isle Royale: *IR* (present), *blank* (absent). ❀ indicates an illustrated species.

Ranunculus acris	**common buttercup**	H	I	IR

❀ common weed of moist fields and clearings; flowers bright yellow, shiny

Ranunculus bulbosus	**bulbous buttercup**	H	I

exotic of fields and disturbed areas; sometimes grown in gardens

Ranunculus fascicularis	**thick-root buttercup**	H	N	IR

in our area, mostly on rock ledges; sometimes in dry openings and woods

Ranunculus flammula	**creeping spearwort**	H	N	IR

aquatic plant, especially in soft water lakes

Ranunculus hispidus	**swamp buttercup**	H	N	IR

ravines; near streams and ponds; swamps

Ranunculus longirostris	**white water-crowfoot**	H	N	IR

lakes, ponds, streams and ditches

T | *Ranunculus macounii* | **marsh-crowfoot** | H | N

in Michigan, known only from Isle Royale

Ranunculus pensylvanicus	**bristly crowfoot**	H	N	IR

wetlands

Ranunculus recurvatus	**hooked crowfoot**	H	N

moist deciduous or mixed forests; swamps

T | *Ranunculus rhomboideus* | **prairie-buttercup** | H | N | IR

Isle Royale; open rocky ridges; a plant of midwestern prairies

Ranunculus sceleratus	**cursed crowfoot**	H	N	IR

❀ mud flats and shores; muddy trails and ruts

Thalictrum dasycarpum	**purple meadow-rue**	H	N	IR

❀ marshy areas, streambanks, peatlands

T | *Thalictrum revolutum* | **skunk meadow-rue** | H | N

plants stout and odorous

▶*Berberidaceae*   Barberry Family

Berberis thunbergii	**Japanese barberry**	S	I

exotic, spread by birds

Caulophyllum thalictroides	**blue cohosh**	H	N

rich deciduous woods; flowers green-yellow to maroon-brown; seeds resemble dark blue berries

▶*Papaveraceae*   Poppy Family

Eschscholzia californica	**California poppy**	H	I

garden escape, collected once near Lake Linden

Papaver orientale	**oriental poppy**	H	I

escape along roads and disturbed places

Papaver rhoeas	**corn poppy**	H	I

waste places

Papaver somniferum	**opium poppy**	H	I

waste places

Sanguinaria canadensis	**bloodroot**	H	N

❀ rich deciduous forest

►*Fumariaceae*   Fumitory Family

Corydalis aurea   **golden corydalis**   H N   IR
❀   rock ledges and ridges, dry forests and disturbed places;
    flowers yellow

Corydalis sempervirens   **pink corydalis**   H N   IR
    rock ledges and ridges, and dry pine forest and disturbed
    areas; flowers pinkish with yellow tips

Dicentra cucullaria   **Dutchman's breeches**   H N   IR
❀   rich deciduous forest; flowers white with 2 long, yellow-tipped
    spurs

(a) Sanguinaria canadensis, (b) Corydalis aurea, (c) Dicentra cucullaria

►*Ulmaceae*   Elm Family

Ulmus americana   **American elm**   T N
    moist to wet forests

►*Cannabaceae*   Indian Hemp Family

Cannabis sativa   **marijuana**   H I
    illegal to cultivate; occurs wild in moist open habitats

Humulus lupulus   **common hops**   S I
    vine; mostly near old homesteads; female flowers used in beer-
    making

►*Urticaceae*   Nettle Family

Laportea canadensis   **wood nettle**   H N
    moist to wet places; stinging hairs

Parietaria pensylvanica **pellitory**   H N
    annual plant of woods and disturbed areas

Urtica dioica   **stinging nettle**   H N/I IR
    stinging hairs on stems and leaves

Lifeform codes: *T* (tree), *S* (shrub), *H* (herbaceous flowering plants), *G* (grasses and grass-like
plants), *F* (ferns and fern-allies). Origin codes: *N* (native to Upper Peninsula), *I* (introduced species).
Present on Isle Royale: *IR* (present), *blank* (absent). ❀ indicates an illustrated species.

▶ *Myricaceae*   Bayberry Family

Comptonia peregrina   **sweetfern**   S   N
     ❀   dry, sandy soil, especially in cut-over areas
Myrica gale   **sweet gale**   S   N   IR
     ❀   peatlands; rocky shores; leaves toothed at end

(a) Comptonia peregrina, (b) Myrica gale

▶ *Fagaceae*   Beech Family

Quercus rubra   **northern red oak**   T   N   IR
     ❀   best growth in rich deciduous forests; leaves with bristle-tipped
        lobes; only native oak in the Keweenaw

Quercus rubra

▶ *Betulaceae*   Birch Family

Alnus incana   **speckled alder**   S   N   IR
     ❀   common shrub of wetlands; also called *Alnus rugosa*
Alnus viridis   **green alder**   S   N   IR
        thicket-forming shrub; often near Lake Superior on dunes or
        rock
Betula alleghaniensis   **yellow birch**   T   N   IR
     ❀   common tree of western U.P. forests; bark shiny yellow-gray,
        shredding in thin curled strips
Betula papyrifera   **paper-birch**   T   N   IR
        characteristic after burns and recent clearings; common in many
        habitats; bark whitish and peeling into wide papery layers

---

Status codes: *E* (endangered in Michigan), *T* (threatened in Michigan), *X* (extirpated from state), *SC* (special concern), *C2* (federal listing may be warranted but more information needed), *3C* (species once proposed for Federal listing but more abundant than previously believed).

Betula pumila   **bog birch, swamp-birch** S N   IR
    peatlands (usually calcium-rich)

Carpinus caroliniana   **hornbeam, ironwood**   S N
    ❀ swamps and moist forests

Corylus cornuta   **beaked hazelnut**   S N   IR
    ❀ common near forest edge and in clearings

Ostrya virginiana   **hop-hornbeam, ironwood** T N   IR
    ❀ small tree of deciduous forests

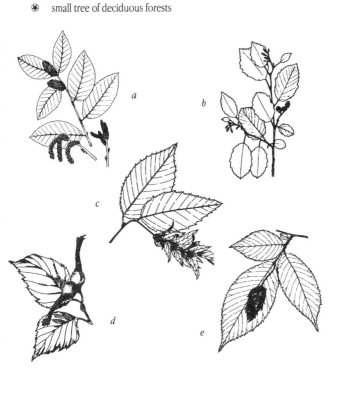

(a) Betula alleghaniensis, (b) Alnus incana, (c) Carpinus caroliniana,
(d) Corylus cornuta, (e) Ostrya virginiana

▶*Nyctaginaceae*   Four-O'clock Family

Mirabilis nyctaginea   **wild four-o'clock**   H I
    dry soil

▶*Chenopodiaceae*   Goosefoot Family

Atriplex patula   **spearscale**   H I
    weedy plant of roadsides; salt-tolerant

Chenopodium album   **lamb's quarters**   H I   IR
    ❀ weed of disturbed places

Chenopodium ambrosioides   **wormseed**   H I
    weedy; strong odor; used to control internal parasites in past

Chenopodium bonus-henricus   **good King Henry**   H I
    edible weed

Chenopodium botrys   **Jerusalem-oak**   H I
    weed of sandy disturbed sites

Lifeform codes: *T* (tree), *S* (shrub), *H* (herbaceous flowering plants), *G* (grasses and grass-like plants), *F* (ferns and fern-allies). Origin codes: *N* (native to Upper Peninsula), *I* (introduced species). Present on Isle Royale: *IR* (present), *blank* (absent). ❀ indicates an illustrated species.

Chenopodium capitatum   **strawberry-blite**   H N IR
found with *Corydalis* in recently disturbed sandy or gravelly places

Chenopodium glaucum   **oak-leaved goosefoot**   H I
weed of disturbed places

Chenopodium hybridum   **goosefoot**   H I
disturbed areas

Chenopodium leptophyllum   **goosefoot**   H I
dry disturbed areas

Chenopodium standleyanum   **woodland-goosefoot**   H N
uncommon, from disturbed areas

Salsola kali   **Russian-thistle**   H I
weed of sandy or cindery disturbed areas

(a) Chenopodium album, (b) Amaranthus retroflexus

►*Amaranthaceae*   Amaranth Family

Amaranthus albus   **tumbleweed**   H N
weed of waste places

Amaranthus blitoides   **amaranth**   H I
common weed of waste places and sandy areas

Amaranthus retroflexus   **redroot, rough pigweed** H I
  ✹   weed of mostly disturbed areas

►*Portulacaceae*   Purslane Family

Claytonia caroliniana   **spring-beauty**   H N IR
  ✹   rich deciduous forests; flowers white or pink with darker veins

Portulaca oleracea   **common purslane**   H I
common weed

Claytonia caroliniana

►*Molluginaceae*   Carpet-weed Family

Mollugo verticillata   **carpetweed**   H   I
   dry sandy soil and dunes

►*Caryophyllaceae*   Pink Family

Agrostemma githago   **corn-cockle**   H   I
   weed of cultivated land

T *Arenaria macrophylla*   **sandwort**   H   N   IR
   Isle Royale, rare; known from rock outcrops

Arenaria serpyllifolia   **thyme-leaf sandwort**   H   I   IR
   weed of sandy or stony soil

Cerastium arvense   **field chickweed**   H   N   IR
   ❀ rocky outcrops and dry sandy woods and fields

Cerastium tomentosum   **snow-in-summer**   H   I   IR
   ornamental; sometimes escaped

Cerastium vulgatum   **mouse-ear chickweed**   H   I   IR
   weed of dry places and woods

Dianthus armeria   **Deptford-pink**   H   I
   sandy fields and clearings

Dianthus barbatus   **sweet william**   H   I   IR
   roadsides, clearings

Dianthus carthusianorum   **cluster-head pink**   H   I
   locally established in Hancock

Dianthus deltoides   **maiden-pink**   H   I
   waste places and near old homesites

Dianthus plumarius   **garden-pink**   H   I   IR
   disturbed areas and old homesites

Gypsophila paniculata   **baby's breath**   H   I
   sandy fields and waste areas

Gypsophila scorzonerifolia   **baby's breath**   H   I
   waste areas, stamp sands

Lychnis chalcedonica   **Maltese-cross**   H   I   IR
   escape from cultivation

Lychnis coronaria   **mullein-pink**   H   I
   escape in open areas and deciduous forest

T *Sagina nodosa*   **pearlwort**   H   N   IR
   moist rock crevices along Lake Superior

Sagina procumbens   **pearlwort**   H   N
   meadows and wet rocks

Saponaria officinalis   **bouncing bet, soapwort** H   I
   sometimes large patches along roadsides and fields

(a) Cerastium arvense, (b) Silene antirhina, (c) Stellaria longifolia

Scleranthus annuus   **knawel**   H   I
    sandy disturbed areas

Silene antirrhina   **sleepy catchfly**   H   N   IR
    ✤   dry sandy places

Silene armeria   **sweet william catchfly**   H   I
    escape of dry open areas

Silene cserei   **bladder-campion**   H   I
    mostly along railroads

Silene latifolia   **white campion**   H   I   IR
    disturbed areas, usually dry

Silene noctiflora   **night-flowering catchfly**   H   I   IR
    open, disturbed sites

Silene vulgaris   **bladder campion**   H   I   IR
    weed of dry, sandy places (often calcium-rich)

Spergula arvensis   **spurrey**   H   I
    disturbed places

Spergularia rubra   **sand-spurrey**   H   I
    dry, sandy disturbed areas

Stellaria aquatica   **giant chickweed**   H   I   IR
    Isle Royale; moist shaded areas; forms tangled masses

Stellaria borealis   **northern stitchwort**   H   N   IR
    moist conifer forests and wetland margins

Stellaria graminea   **common stitchwort**   H   I   IR
    moist disturbed areas

Stellaria longifolia   **long-leaved stitchwort**   H   N   IR
    ✤   swamps, marshes, and along ponds and creeks

Stellaria media   **common chickweed**   H   I   IR
    common weed of disturbed places

Vaccaria hispanica   **cow-herb**   H   I
    uncommon weed of waste areas

▶ *Polygonaceae*   Smartweed Family

Fagopyrum esculentum   **buckwheat**   H   I
    occasional escape from cultivation

Polygonella articulata   **jointweed**   H   N
    jack pine plains and sand dunes

Polygonum achoreum   **smartweed**   H   I?   IR
    weed of sandy or gravelly places

Polygonum amphibium   **water smartweed**   H   N/I   IR
    ✤   lakes and ponds; pink flowers on short spike

(a) Polygonum amphibium, (b) Polygonum hydropiper, (c) P. hydropiperoides

Polygonum aviculare   knotweed   H N IR
    weed of disturbed areas

Polygonum cilinode   fringed bindweed   H N IR
    plant mostly of recently cleared areas

Polygonum convolvulus   black bindweed   H I IR
    weed of waste places

Polygonum cuspidatum   Japanese knotweed   H I
    escaped ornamental; plants to six feet or more

Polygonum douglasii   smartweed   H N IR
    dry rock outcrops; disjunct from western US

Polygonum erectum   knotweed   H N
    farmyards and waste places

Polygonum hydropiper   water-pepper   H I
    ❀ wetlands; most common in disturbed wet places

Polygonum hydropiperoides false water-pepper   H N
    ❀ wetlands and shallow water

Polygonum lapathifolium dock-leaved smartweed   H N/I IR
    ❀ moist soil

Polygonum pensylvanicum   Penns. smartweed   H N
    moist soil of wetlands or fields

Polygonum persicaria   lady's thumb   H I
    ❀ weed of moist to dry places

Polygonum punctatum   dotted smartweed   H N IR
    wet soil and shallow water; sometimes shaded

Polygonum sachalinense   giant knotweed   H I
    rarely escaped ornamental

Polygonum sagittatum   arrow-leaved tearthumb H N IR
    sprawling plants sometimes forming a distinct zone in wetlands;
    stems 4-sided with prickles along each angle; flowers pinkish

T *Polygonum viviparum*   alpine bistort   H N IR
    ❀ rock crevices along Lake Superior

(a) Polygonum lapathifolium, (b) P. persicaria, (c) P. viviparum

Rheum rhabarbicum   rhubarb   H I
    persistent around old farmsteads

Rumex acetosella   red sorrel   H I IR
    troublesome weed forming large colonies, especially on sandy
    soils

Rumex crispus   curly dock   H I IR
    weeed of clearings and disturbed places

Rumex longifolius   yard-dock   H I IR
    uncommon weed of moist places

Rumex obtusifolius   bitter dock   H I IR
    weed of moist soil and clearings

Rumex orbiculatus   great-water-dock   H N IR
    often large plant of wetlands

Rumex salicifolius   **dock**   H N IR
     marshy areas, ditches, and clearings

►*Elatinaceae*   Waterwort Family

Elatine minima   **waterwort**   H N
     submersed in shallow water, forming moss-like mats

►*Clusiaceae*   Mangosteen Family

Hypericum boreale   **St. John's-wort**   H N IR
     peatlands and shorelines

Hypericum ellipticum   **St. John's-wort**   H N
     moist wetland margins

Hypericum majus   **St. John's-wort**   H N IR
     ❀   wetlands and shorelines

Hypericum perforatum   **common St. John's-wort**   H I IR
     ❀   common weed of fields, waste places, and rocks; leaves
     perforated with tiny holes

Hypericum pyramidatum   **giant St. John's-wort**   H N
     plants up to 6 feet tall; wetlands

Triadenum fraseri   **marsh St. John's-wort**   H N IR
     ❀   occurs in many types of wetlands stem and lower leaves reddish
     and smooth; leaves opposite and without stems (petioles);
     flowers pink-red

 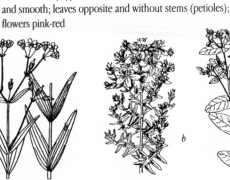 

(a)Hypericum majus, (b) Hypericum perforatum, (c) Triadenum fraseri

►*Tiliaceae*   Linden Family

Tilia americana   **basswood, American linden**   T N
     ❀   rich deciduous forests and swamps; large heart-shaped leaves
     with one lobe lower than other; fragrant yellow flowers

Tilia americana

Status codes: *E* (endangered in Michigan), *T* (threatened in Michigan), *X* (extirpated from state), *SC* (special concern), *C2* (federal listing may be warranted but more information needed), *3C* (species once proposed for Federal listing but more abundant than previously believed).

▶*Malvaceae*   Mallow Family

Althaea rosea   **hollyhock**   H   I
     escaped ornamental
Malva moschata   **musk-mallow**   H   I
     roadsides, dry fields and clearings
Malva neglecta   **common mallow**   H   I
  ❀   common weed of waste places
Malva sylvestris   **high mallow**   H   I
     uncommon escape along roadsides and in fields

(a) Malva neglecta, (b) Sarracenia pupurea

▶*Sarraceniaceae*   Pitcher-plant Family

Sarracenia purpurea   **pitcher-plant**   H   N   IR
  ❀   common insectivorous plants of sphagnum peatlands and
     tamarack swamps; inner surface of water-filled pitcher with
     downward pointing hairs to trap insects

▶*Droseraceae*   Sundew Family

SC **Drosera anglica**   **great sundew**   H   N   IR
  ❀   mostly calcium-rich peatlands and wet areas; glistening glands
     of sundew leaves attract and trap insects
Drosera intermedia   **intermediate sundew**   H   N   IR
     wet areas in peatlands; survives periodic inundation
Drosera linearis   **linear-leaved sundew**   H   N   IR
     marly peatlands; usually not growing in sphagnum; leaves strap-
     like
Drosera rotundifolia   **round-leaved sundew**   H   N   IR
  ❀   swamps and fens, usually on sphagnum hummocks or logs; our
     most common sundew; leaves round

(a) Drosera anglica, (b) Drosera rotundifolia

Lifeform codes: *T* (tree), *S* (shrub), *H* (herbaceous flowering plants), *G* (grasses and grass-like
plants, *F* (ferns and fern-allies). Origin codes: *N* (native to Upper Peninsula), *I* (introduced species).
Present on Isle Royale: *IR* (present), *blank* (absent). ❀ indicates an illustrated species.

►*Cistaceae*   Rock-rose Family

Hudsonia tomentosa   **beach-heath**   S N
⚜ dry sandy open woods and dunes; low mat-forming shrub to 8
   inches; resembles a juniper but with many yellow flowers on
   branch ends; Great Sand Bay

Hudsonia tomentosa

►*Violaceae*   Violet Family

Viola adunca   **hook-spurred violet**   H N   IR
⚜ dry sandy open forests; rock outcrops and shorelines; flowers
   violet
Viola arvensis   **European field-pansy** H I
   weed of dry, sandy places
Viola blanda   **sweet white violet**   H N   IR
   moist forests and swamps; flowers white with purple veins
Viola canadensis   **tall white violet**   H N
⚜ moist forests; flowers white

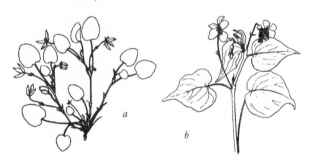

(a) Viola adunca, (b) Viola canadensis

Viola conspersa   **American dog-violet**   H N   IR
   moist forests and swamps; clearings; flowers pale violet with
   white center; basal leaves dry early in season
Viola cucullata   **blue marsh violet**   H N   IR
   swamps and fens; low areas in hardwood forests; flowers violet,
   darker near center
T **Viola epipsila**   **northern marsh violet** H N
   In Michigan, known only from moist woods on Manitou Island off
   tip of Keweenaw Peninsula; flowers light blue to lilac
Viola lanceolata   **lance-leaved violet**   H N
   wet, sandy or peaty soil; distinctive lance-shaped leaves 1 to 4
   inches long

Status codes: *E* (endangered in Michigan), *T* (threatened in Michigan), *X* (extirpated from state),
SC (special concern), *C2* (federal listing may be warranted but more information needed), *3C*
(species once proposed for Federal listing but more abundant than previously believed).

Viola macloskeyi　　　　**wild white violet**　　H　N　IR
　　　wet places and hollows; flowers white

Viola nepbropbylla　　　**marsh violet**　　　H　N　IR
　　　wetlands; moist rocky shores; prefers calcium-rich sites;
　　　flowers violet, darker at center

Viola odorata　　　　　**English or sweet violet** H　I
　　　garden escape

Viola pubescens　　　　**yellow forest- violet**　H　N　IR
　　　deciduous and mixed woods; flowers yellow with purple veins

Viola renifolia　　　　　**kidney-leaved violet**　H　N　IR
❀　　most common in cedar swamps; flowers white with purple
　　　veins

Viola sagittata　　　　**arrowhead-violet**　　H　N
　　　dry to moist sandy woods and fields; flowers blue-violet

Viola selkirkii　　　　　**great-spurred violet**　H　N　IR
　　　rich deciduous forests; rotting logs and crevices; flowers violet

Viola sororia　　　　　**common blue violet**　H　N　IR
❀　　dry to wet deciduous woods; flowers blue

Viola tricolor　　　　　**Johnny-jump-up**　　H　I
　　　garden escape

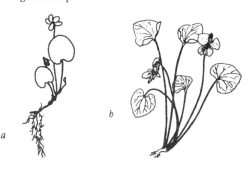

(a) Viola renifolia, (b) Viola sororia

▶*Curcurbitaceae*　　　　Gourd Family

Echinocystis lobata　　**balsam-apple, wild cucumber** H　N
　　　moist forests and streambanks

▶*Salicaceae*　　　　　　Willow Family

Populus alba　　　　　**white or silver poplar**　T　I
　　　cultivated; spreading by suckers

Populus balsamifera　　**balsam-poplar**　　　T　N　IR
❀　　swamps, sand dunes and interdunal hollows; may form large
　　　thickets

Populus grandidentata　**bigtoothed- aspen**　T　N　IR
　　　common tree of sandy soils, cut-over areas, young forests

Populus tremuloides　　**quaking aspen**　　T　N　IR
❀　　common tree of moist or wet forests, cut-over areas

Salix bebbiana　　　**Bebb's willow, beaked willow** S　N
　　　common willow of wet areas

Salix discolor　　　　　**pussy-willow**　　　S　N　IR
❀　　common willow of wet areas

Lifeform codes: *T* (tree), *S* (shrub), *H* (herbaceous flowering plants), *G* (grasses and grass-like plants, *F* (ferns and fern-allies). Origin codes: *N* (native to Upper Peninsula), *I* (introduced species). Present on Isle Royale: *IR* (present), *blank* (absent). ❀ indicates an illustrated species.

(a) *Populus balsamifera,* (b) *Populus tremuloides,* (c) *Salix discolor,*
(d) *Salix exigua,* (e) *Salix lucida,* (f) *Salix pedicillaris,* (g) *Salix petiolaris,*
(b) *Salix serissima*

Salix eriocephala	**diamond-willow**	S	N	
wetlands and dunes				
Salix exigua	**sandbar willow**	S	N	
❀ streambanks, diches, dunes; often forms large thickets				
Salix fragilis	**brittle willow**	S	I	
introduced tree sometimes found in wet places and streambanks				
Salix humilis	**prairie willow**	S	N	IR
dry sandy or rocky places				
Salix lucida	**shining willow**	S	N	IR
❀ wetlands, hollows in dunes				

Status codes: *E* (endangered in Michigan), *T* (threatened in Michigan), *X* (extirpated from state), *SC* (special concern), *C2* (federal listing may be warranted but more information needed), *3C* (species once proposed for Federal listing but more abundant than previously believed).

Salix nigra   **black willow**   T/S   N
     shrub or tree along streams

Salix pedicillaris   **bog-willow**   S   N   IR
     ❀   peatlands

SC *Salix pellita*   **satiny willow**   S   N   IR
     uncommon willow on streambanks, sandy shores and moist, rocky hollows

Salix pentandra   **laurel willow**   T/S   I
     introduced shrub or tree in fields, dunes, and streambanks

Salix petiolaris   **mdow-willow**   S   N   IR
     ❀   open places in wetlands

T *Salix planifolia*   **plane-leaved willow**   S   N   IR
     boreal species known in Michigan only from Isle Royale

Salix pyrifolia   **balsam-willow**   S   N   IR
     peatlands, rock outcrops, and roadsides

Salix serissima   **autumn-willow**   S   N
     ❀   late-flowering willow of swamps and fens; often on calcium-rich sites

▶*Brassicaceae*   Mustard Family

Arabis caucasica   **wall rock cress**   H   I
     escape from gardens

Arabis divaricarpa   **rock cress**   H   N   IR
     sandy or rocky soil, ridgetops, margins of aspen groves

Arabis drummondii   **rock cress**   H   N   IR
     Isle Royale; rocky openings

Arabis glabra   **tower-mustard**   H   N   IR
     dry sandy open woods, fields, rocky ridgetops

Arabis birsuta   **rock cress**   H   N   IR
     found in many moist to dry, often calcium-rich habitats; rock outcrops

Arabis bolboellii   **rock cress**   H   N   IR
     rocky ridges; dry sand dunes

Arabis laevigata   **rock cress**   H   N
     moist, rich hardwood forests

Arabis lyrata   **sand cress**   H   N   IR
     ❀   rock outcrops and sand dunes

(a) Arabis lyrata, (b) Braya bumilis

Armoracia rusticana   **horse-radish**   H   I   IR
     garden escape on moist soil

Barbarea ortboceras   **yellow rocket**   H   N   IR
     Isle Royale; gravelly or rocky shores

Barbarea vulgaris   **yellow rocket**   H   I   IR
     common exotic weed of disturbed areas and sometimes woods

Berteroa incana   **hoary alyssum**   H   I   IR
     weed of roadsides and sometimes dry woods

Brassica juncea   **brown or Indian mustard**   H   I
     weed of waste places

Brassica napus   **rape, rutabaga**   H   I
     escaped from cultivation

Brassica nigra   **black mustard**   H   I
     cultivated and sometimes escaped

Brassica rapa   **field mustard**   H   I
     weed of fields and disturbed areas

T   *Braya bumilis*   **braya**   H   N   IR
     ❀   boreal/arctic species known in Michigan only from rocks on
     Isle Royale and Copper Harbor

Camelina sativa   **false flax**   H   I
     uncommon weed; rarely collected

Capsella bursa-pastoris   **shepherd's purse**   H   I   IR
     early blooming weed of roadsides, fields, waste places

Cardamine concatenata   **cut-leaved toothwort**   H   N
     moist hardwood forests

Cardamine diphylla   **two-leaved toothwort**   H   N
     moist forests or cedar swamps

Cardamine flexuosa   **bitter-cress**   H   I
     exotic of moist areas

Cardamine parviflora   **dryland bitter-cress**   H   N   IR
     rocky ridgetops and shores

Cardamine pensylvanica   **Penns. bitter-cress**   H   N   IR
     ❀   swamps, ditches, wet trails

Conringia orientalis   **hare's-ear mustard**   H   I
     exotic of waste areas and gardens

Descurainia pinnata   **tansy-mustard**   H   N?
     roadsides, fields, gravel pits

Diplotaxis muralis   **sand-rocket, wall-rocket**   H   I
     sandy or gravelly disturbed areas

T   *Draba arabisans*   **draba**   H   N   IR
     uncommon boreal plant of rock outcrops

T   *Draba glabella*   **draba**   H   N   IR
     Isle Royale, uncommon; rock outcrops

T   *Draba incana*   **draba**   H   N   IR
     in Michigan, known only from Passage Island and Gull Island off
     Isle Royale

Erucastrum gallicum   **dog-mustard**   H   I
     weed of roadsides and waste places

(a) Cardamine pensylvanica, (b) Rorippa nasturtium-aquaticum

Erysimum cheiranthoides **wormseed-mustard** H I IR
usually in moist disturbed places

Erysimum hieraciifolium **tall wormseed-mustard** H I
uncommon exotic

Erysimum inconspicuum **wallflower** H I IR
dry disturbed areas and rock outcrops; native of western US

Hesperis matronalis **dame's rocket** H I
garden escape along roads and moist areas

Lepidium campestre **field-cress** H I IR
exotic weed of disturbed areas and sometimes dry woods

Lepidium densiflorum **prairie-pepperweed** H I IR
weed of disturbed areas and dry, open woods

Lepidium virginicum **poor-man's pepper** H N
weed of dry sandy or gravelly areas

Lobularia maritima **sweet alyssum** H I
garden escape

Rorippa curvipes **yellow-cress** H I
uncommon weed; in Michigan, known only from single
Houghton County collection

Rorippa nasturtium-aquaticum **water-cress** H I
❀ edible plant of cold springs and streams

Rorippa palustris **common yellow-cress** H N IR
wet places, muddy shores, roadsides

Sinapis alba **white mustard** H I
naturalized weed of waste places

Sinapis arvensis **charlock** H I IR
common weed of fields and waste places

Sisymbrium altissimum **tumbling mustard** H I IR
weed of dry places

Sisymbrium officinale **hedge-mustard** H I
weed of roadsides and disturbed areas

T *Subularia aquatica* **awlwort** H N IR
uncommon in Michigan; plant of shallow water at Rock Harbor,
Isle Royale

Thlaspi arvense **field penny-cress** H I IR
weed of waste places

▶*Empetraceae*   Crowberry Family

T *Empetrum nigrum* **black crowberry** S N IR
❀ uncommon in Michigan; occurs on rock and in cedar or black
spruce swamps

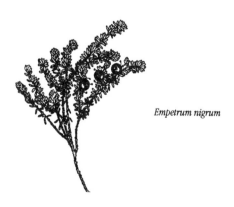

Empetrum nigrum

(a) *Andromeda glaucophylla*, (b) *Arctostaphyllos uva-ursi*, (c) *Chamaedaphne calyculata*, (d) *Epigea repens*, (e) *Gaultheria hispidula*, (f) *Gaultheria procumbens*, (g) *Gaylussacia baccata*, (h) *Kalmia polifolia*, (i) *Ledum groenlandicum*

Status codes: *E* (endangered in Michigan), *T* (threatened in Michigan), *X* (extirpated from state), *SC* (special concern), *C2* (federal listing may be warranted but more information needed), *3C* (species once proposed for Federal listing but more abundant than previously believed).

►*Ericaceae*   Heath Family

Andromeda glaucophylla   **bog-rosemary**   S   N   IR
- ✸ common low shrub of acidic peatlands; leaves narrow and held erect, shiny above and white below; flowers urn-shaped and pinkish

Arctostaphylos uva-ursi   **bearberry, kinnickinnick**   S   N   IR
- ✸ dry sandy or rocky soil, sand dunes; trailing low evergreen shrub, mat-forming; leaves thick, glossy on top surface; fruit a dull red berry

Chamaedaphne calyculata   **leatherleaf**   S   N   IR
- ✸ ubiquitous shrub of open peatlands; leaves evergreen, shiny above, rusty below; upper leaves reduced in size

Epigea repens   **trailing arbutus**   S   N
- ✸ dry, sandy or rocky, acidic soil; trailing low shrub; leaves hairy with net-like veins; flowers pink or white, tubular, in clusters

Gaultheria hispidula   **creeping snowberry**   S   N   IR
- ✸ peatlands, often on hummocks and logs; trailing small shrub; leaves small and shiny above; flowers small and greenish-white; fruit a small white edible berry

Gaultheria procumbens   **wintergreen**   S   N   IR
- ✸ dry or moist acidic woods

Gaylussacia baccata   **black huckleberry**   S   N
- ✸ dry rocky woods; peatlands; shrub to 3 feet; leaves with shiny yellow sticky spots; flowers pink and resinous; fruit a smooth dark blue berry; edible

Kalmia polifolia   **swamp-laurel**   S   N   IR
- ✸ low shrub of peatlands; leaves leathery with rolled over margins, shiny above, whitish below; flowers pink in small cluster

Ledum groenlandicum   **Labrador-tea**   S   N   IR
- ✸ common shrub in swamps and wet margins; young shoots and leaves covered with wooly brown hairs; leaf margins rolled under

Vaccinium angustifolium   **lowbush-blueberry**   S   N   IR
- small shrub (to 1 foot) of sandy or rocky soil, dunes, burned-over sites; forming large patches; flowers white, bell-shaped; fruit a smooth waxy blue berry favored by bear and other mammals

T   ***Vaccinium cespitosum***   **dwarf bilberry**   S   N
        uncommon in Michigan; rocky woods and lake shores

Vaccinium corymbosum   highbush-blueberry   S   N
        usually in swamps and fens

Vaccinium macrocarpon   **cranberry**   S   N   IR
- ✸ hummocks in swamps and fens; similar to *V. oxycoccos* but with larger, broader leaves, only slightly white below; harvested commercially in Wisconsin and New England

Vaccinium membranaceum   **mountain-bilberry**   S   N
- ✸ moist forests

(a) Vaccinium membranaceum, (b) Vaccinium ovalifolium

Lifeform codes: *T* (tree), *S* (shrub), *H* (herbaceous flowering plants), *G* (grasses and grass-like plants, *F* (ferns and fern-allies). Origin codes: *N* (native to Upper Peninsula), *I* (introduced species). Present on Isle Royale: *IR* (present), *blank* (absent). ✸ indicates an illustrated species.

Vaccinium myrtilloides **velvetleaf-blueberry** S N IR
  dry rocky woods and openings; plants 1-2 feet high; covered
  with soft hairs; fruit bright blue

Vaccinium ovalifolium **tall bilberry** S N
  ❀ moist woods

Vaccinium oxycoccos **small cranberry** S N IR
  ❀ hummmocks in sphagnum peatlands; small trailing plants;
  leaves narrow and small, glossy above, white below; berries
  shiny red, persistent

Vaccinium pallidum **hillside-blueberry** S N IR
  dry upland woods and old fields

T *Vaccinium uliginosum* **bog-bilberry** S N IR
  rare; rocky shore of Lake Superior

X *Vaccinium vitis-idaea* **lingonberry, partridge-berry** S N IR
  in Michigan, once known from Keweenaw Peninsula and Isle
  Royale; may be extinct from state; plants evergreen, creeping,
  forming mats 2-3 inches tall; leaves shiny above; black dots on
  underside; fruits bright red cluster of berries

(a) Vaccinium macrocarpon, (b) Vaccinium oxycoccos

▶*Pyrolaceae*   Shinleaf Family

Chimaphila umbellata **princes's pine, pipsissewa** S N IR
  ❀ dry sandy woods; leaves evergreen, shiny; flowers waxy, creamy
  or pink

Moneses uniflora **wood nymph** H N IR
  ❀ diminutive plant of moist or wet forests, 2-6 inches tall; single
  waxy-white drooping flower

Pyrola asarifolia **pink shinleaf** H N IR
  ❀ moist forests; broad leathery leaves, shiny on top surface;
  flowers pink-red

Pyrola chlorantha **shinleaf** S N IR
  hardwood and conifer forests

Pyrola elliptica **elliptic shinleaf** H N IR
  conifer forests and rocky slopes; leaves not shiny; flowers white
  with light green veins, waxy

Pyrola rotundifolia **rounded shinleaf** H N IR
  hardwood and conifer forests; shiny evergreen leaves; flowers
  white or pinkish

Pyrola secunda **one-sided shinleaf** S N IR
  ❀ moist hardwood and conifer forests; shiny leaves; green-white
  flowers on one side of stalk

Status codes: *E* (endangered in Michigan), *T* (threatened in Michigan), *X* (extirpated from state),
SC (special concern), *C2* (federal listing may be warranted but more information needed), *3C*
(species once proposed for Federal listing but more abundant than previously believed).

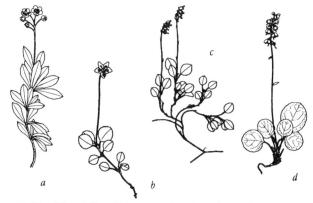

(a) Chimaphila umbellata, (b) Moneses uniflora, (c) Pyrola secunda,
(d) Pyrola asarifolia

►*Monotropaceae*   Indian Pipe Family

Monotropa hypopithys   **sweet pinesap**   H   N
- ✤ uncommon saprophyte of usually acidic, mixed forests; plants lack chlorophyll

Monotropa uniflora   **Indian pipe**   H   N
- ✤ uncommon saprophyte of forests; waxy-white plants lack chlorophyll; leaves reduced to scales along stem; plants turn black when dry

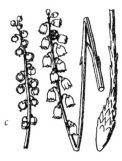

(a) Monotropa hypopithys, (b) Monotropa uniflora, (c) Pterospora andromedea

T   ***Pterospora andromedea***   **pine-drops**   H   N
- ✤ uncommon plant of dry conifer forests

►*Primulaceae*   Primrose Family

Lysimachia ciliata   **fringed loosestrife**   H   N   IR
Isle Royale; wetland margins, other moist to wet places; flowers yellow, usually nodding, with 5 pointed petals

Lysimachia terrestris   **swamp candles**   H   N   IR
common in wetlands; opposite leaves with black spots on both sides; flowers yellow with red streaks

Lysimachia thrysifolia   **swamp-loosestrife**   H   N   IR
- ✤ common in swamps and along streams; yellow flowers

Primula mistassinica   **Mistassini primrose**   H   N   IR
- ✤ rocks crevices along Lake Superior; plants 6-10 inches tall from small rosette; flowers pink with yellow center; five notched petals

54

Trientalis borealis **starflower** H N IR
- ❁ hardwood and conifer forests; peatlands; single upright stem 6-10 inches tall, topped by whorl of leaves; one or several white flowers above, petals sharp-pointed

(a) Lysimachia thrysifolia, (b) Primula mistassinica, (c) Trientalis borealis

►*Grossulariaceae* Gooseberry Family

Ribes americanum **eastern black currant** S N
- ❁ moist forests and swamps; fruit black; fruit and lower leaf surface with small resinous spots

Ribes cynosbati **dogberry** S N
- ❁ rich deciduous forests; also swamps and dry woods; fruit and nodes with stiff prickles

Ribes glandulosum **skunk-currant** S N IR
- ❁ swamps and wet places in deciduous forests; fruit red or yellow; stems and fruit with gland-tipped hairs

Ribes hirtellum **swamp gooseberry** S N
- ❁ cedar and tamarack swamps, streambanks; canes and fruit mostly smooth (without bristles)

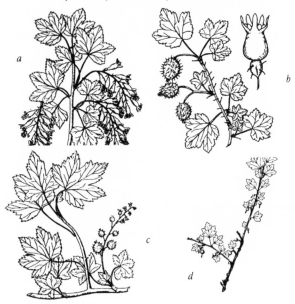

(a) Ribes americanum, (b) Ribes cynobasti, (c) Ribes glandulosum, (d) Ribes hirtellum

Ribes budsonianum   **western black currant**   S   N   IR
     most common in cedar swamps; fruit black; fruit and lower leaf surface with resin dots

Ribes lacustre   **spiny swamp-currant**   S   N   IR
     ❀   moist, shady conifer or mixed forest; canes with bristles and prickles; fruit black with gland-tipped bristles

Ribes nigrum   **black currant**   S   I
     garden escape; fruit used in jams and jellies

Ribes odoratum   **buffalo-currant**   S   I
     escape from cultivation

SC *Ribes oxyacanthoides*   **northern gooseberry**   S   N   IR
     ❀   rocky ridgetops and clearings; fruit smooth, canes bristly; leaves with glands

Ribes sativum   **garden red currant**   S   I
     garden escape; grown for its berries

Ribes triste   **swamp red currant**   S   N   IR
     swamps and wet hollows in deciduous forests; flowers on old wood, below current year's growth; small fruit smooth and hard

(a) Ribes lacustre, (b) Ribes oxyacanthoides

▶*Crassulaceae*   Stonecrop Family

Sedum acre   **golden carpet**   H   I   IR
     mat-forming plant of sand dunes, fields, and roadsides

Sedum purpureum   **live-forever**   H   I
     garden escape mostly near old homesteads

▶*Saxifragaceae*   Saxifrage Family

Chrysoplenium americanum   **golden saxifrage**   H   N
     ❀   forming large mats along streams and in swamps

Mitella nuda   **naked mitrewort**   H   N   IR
     ❀   cedar swamps and moist forests; often on moss

T   *Parnassia palustris*   **arctic grass-of-parnassus**   H   N   IR
     ❀   wet places, often on calcium-rich soil

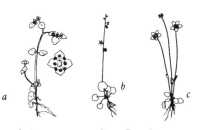

(a) Chrysoplenium americanum, (b) Mitella nuda, (c) Parnassia palustris

Penthorum sedoides   **ditch-stonecrop**   H   N
    marshes, streambanks, pond margins

T   *Saxifraga aizoon*   **lime-crusted saxifrage**   H   N   IR
    boreal plant known in Michigan only from rocky Lake Superior
    shoreline of Isle Royale

Saxifraga pensylvanica   **swamp-saxifrage**   H   N
    wet forests and swamps; often on calcium-rich soil

T   *Saxifraga tricuspidata*   **three-toothed saxifrage**   H   N   IR
    arctic species known in Michigan only from rocks on Isle Royale

Saxifraga virginiensis   **early saxifrage**   H   N   IR
    rock crevices and outcrops

▶*Rosaceae*   Rose Family

Agrimonia gryposepala   **common agrimony**   H   N
    ❀   moist to wet woods, openings and old fields; flowers yellow in
    long clusters; seed bristly and attaches to clothing or animals

Agrimonia striata   **roadside-agrimony**   H   N   IR
    moist to dry woods; swamps

Amelanchier arborea   **downy serviceberry**   S   N   IR
    dry woods and rocky openings; less common in moist woods;
    serviceberry fruit favored by birds and many mammals

Amelanchier bartramiana   **mountain serviceberry**   S   N   IR
    ❀   spruce and tamarack swamps; rocky or sandy shores and ridges

Amelanchier interior   **serviceberry**   S   N   IR
    wooded dunes and rocky outcrops

Amelanchier laevis   **smooth serviceberry**   S   N   IR
    dry sandy woods and shores; rocky areas

Amelanchier sanguinea   **New England s.**   S   N   IR
    dry sandy open woods and dunes

Amelanchier spicata   **dwarf serviceberry**   S   N
    dry jack pine or oak woods; dunes; often with *Comptonia* and
    Vaccinium

Aronia prunifolia   **chokeberry**   S   N   IR
    ❀   widespread shrub of swamps, fens, and other wetlands; flowers
    white with dark red anthers; fruit black and persistent, little
    eaten by wildlife

C2 *Chamaerhodos erecta*   **Keweenaw rock-rose**   H   N
/E   ❀   in Michigan, known only from Brockway Mountain; disjunct
    from main range in western North America; also known as
    Chamaerhodos nuttallii var. *keweenawensis*

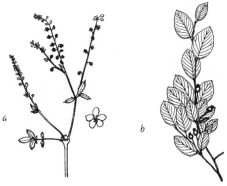

(a) Agrimonia gryposepela, (b) Amelanchier bartramiana

Crataegus chrysocarpa   **fireberry-hawthorn**   S   N
  forming thickets on sandy soil and dunes; fields and clearings;
  most hawthorns have thorny branches and orange or red fruit;
  species often difficult to distinguish

SC *Crataegus douglasii*   **black hawthorn**   T   N   IR
  ❀   sand dunes and shores, rocky woods and outcrops; locally
  common near Delaware location; disjunct from western US

Crataegus flabellata   **fanleaf-hawthorn**   S   N
  dry sandy woods and rock outcrops

Crataegus monogyna   **oneseed-hawthorn**   T   I
  occasional escape to fields and roadsides

Crataegus succulenta   **fleshy hawthorn**   S   N
  woods, field, fencerows

(a) Aronia prunifolia, (b) Chamaerbodos erecta, (c) Crataegus douglasii

Fragaria vesca   **woodland strawberry**   H   N   IR
  moist forests and rocky areas; swamps

Fragaria virginiana   **wild strawberry**   H   N   IR
  common plant of moist to dry forests; clearings and disturbed
  areas; edible fruit

Geum aleppicum   **yellow avens**   H   N   IR
  swamps and moist forests; common along trails and in
  clearings; plants hairy; flowers deep yellow

Geum canadense   **white avens**   H   N
  moist deciduous forests and swamps; flowers white; fruit bur-like

Geum macrophyllum   **big-leaved avens**   H   N
  deciduous forests; clearings

Geum rivale   **water avens**   H   N   IR
  ❀   fens and swamps; flowers purplish, nodding

Physocarpus opulifolius   **ninebark**   S   N   IR
  ❀   rock outcrops; occasionally in swamps and along streams;
  flowers in white rounded clusters; fruit purplish-brown pods
  persisting into winter

Potentilla anserina   **silver-weed**   H   N   IR
  ❀   pond and lake edges, marshes; plants with surface runners;
  leaves many-parted; silvery beneath; single yellow flowers.

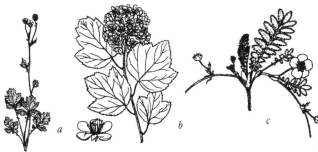

(a) Geum rivale, (b) Physocarpus opulifolius, (c) Potentilla anserina

Potentilla argentea   **silvery-cinquefoil**   H I   IR
dry sandy disturbed areas

Potentilla arguta   **tall cinquefoil**   H N? IR
dry sandy places; rocky outcrops and shorelines

Potentilla flabelliformis   **comb cinquefoil**   H I
native to western North America; uncommon in Michigan

Potentilla fruticosa   **shrubby cinquefoil**   S N   IR
shorelines, tamarack swamps, fens; especially on alkaline sites;
small twiggy shrub with shredding bark; flowers yellow

Potentilla hippiana   **woolly cinquefoil**   H I
in Michigan, known from disturbed ground at mine near
Calumet; common in western US

Potentilla inclinata   **cinquefoil**   H I
weed of sandy disturbed places and fields; similar to *P. argentea*
and *P. recta*

Potentilla norvegica   **strawberry-weed, rough c.** H N/I IR
disturbed places, meadows and rocks; moist or dry

Potentilla palustris   **marsh-cinquefoil**   H N   IR
  ❀   peatlands and marshes, often in shallow water; leaves 5-7
parted, sharp-toothed; flowers reddish

Potentilla palustris

T *Potentilla pensylvanica*   **prairie cinquefoil**   H N   IR
rock outcrops; more common to north and west

Potentilla recta   **sulfur cinquefoil**   H I   IR
aggressively spreading European weed

Potentilla simplex   **old-field or common cinquefoil** H N   IR
dry, open sandy woods; fields, and rock ledges

Potentilla tridentata   **three-toothed cinquefoil** H N   IR
rocky shoreline, dry sandy jack pine and oak forests; in U.P.
locally abundant along south shore of Lake Superior; leathery
leaves with 3 leaflets, toothed at tips; flowers white

Prunus cerasus   **sour cherry, pie-cherry** S I
large shrub in old fields and fencerows

Prunus domestica   **common plum**   S I
old fields and fencerows

Prunus nigra   **Canada-plum**   S N
deciduous forests; streambanks; leaves with glan-tipped teeth;
two glands on petiole; flowers white to reddish; fruit orange-
red and tasty when ripe

Prunus pensylvanica   **pin-cherry**   S N   IR
young forests of aspen, birch, or jack pine; characteristic
following fire or clearing; shiny red-brown bark; leave petioles
with glands; fruit light red, favored by birds

Prunus pumila   **sand-cherry**   S N
jack pine and oak woods, dunes, and rocky areas; fruit purple-
black

Prunus serotina   **wild black cherry**   T N
fencerows and forest margins; seeds spread by birds; can be
large tree in rich woods

Status codes: *E* (endangered in Michigan), *T* (threatened in Michigan), *X* (extirpated from state),
SC (special concern), *C2* (federal listing may be warranted but more information needed), *3C*
(species once proposed for Federal listing but more abundant than previously believed).

Prunus virginiana   **choke-cherry**   S N IR

❀ common in all but very wet habitats; flowers in racemes, cream colored; fruit deep red or purple, tart

Prunus virginiana

Pyrus malus   **apple**   T I IR

common apple; old fields, roadsides

Rosa acicularis   **bristly rose**   S N IR

❀ sandy jack pine and oak woods, dunes, rocks; prickly stems

Rosa arkansana   **dwarf prairie-rose**   S N IR

fields, roadsides, streambanks

Rosa blanda   **smooth rose**   S N IR

❀ dry jack pine woods, dunes, rock outcrops, fields; stems with only scattered prickles; flowers pink

(a) Rosa acicularis, (b) Rosa blanda

Rosa eglanteria   **sweetbrier**   S I

very thorny; fields, roadsides, streambanks

Rosa majalis   **cinnamon rose**   S I

escape near old farms and fields

Rosa palustris   **swamp-rose**   S N

swamps, fens, pond margins

Rosa pimpinellifolia   **Scotch rose**   S I

occasional escape into fields and roadsides

Rosa rugosa   **Japanese rose**   S I

ornamental rarely escaped into fields and disturbed areas

Rubus alleghaniensis   **common blackberry**   S N

old fields, roadsides; robust canes with sharp thorns; black edible fruit

Rubus canadensis   **smooth blackberry**   S N

old fields, clearings

Rubus flagellaris   **northern dewberry**   S N

sandy, dry to moist woods; meadows

Rubus hispidus   **swamp-dewberry**   S N

mostly in damp, shaded wetlands; marsh edges

Rubus idaeus   **wild red raspberry**   S N IR

common in moist to dry woods and openings, especially after clearing or fire; canes prickly

Rubus parviflorus   **thimbleberry**   S N IR

❀ thicket-forming in openings in moist hardwood or mixed forests; leaves large and maple-like; thornless; flowers white

---

Lifeform codes: *T* (tree), *S* (shrub), *H* (herbaceous flowering plants), *G* (grasses and grass-like plants), *F* (ferns and fern-allies). Origin codes: *N* (native to Upper Peninsula), *I* (introduced species). Present on Isle Royale: *IR* (present), *blank* (absent). ❀ indicates an illustrated species.

Rubus pensilvanicus   **Penns. blackberry**   S N IR
    moist swamp and marsh borders; fields and roadsides

Rubus pubescens   **dwarf raspberry**   S N IR
    ✿   moist woods and swamps; rocky openings and ledges; plants
    trailing and thornless; berry divided into only a few parts

Rubus setosus   **bristly blackberry**   S N
    sandy fields and woods; wooded dunes; wetland margins

Sorbus americana   **American mountain-ash**   T N
    cedar and deciduous swamps, mixed forest; fruit smaller than
    Sorbus decora

Sorbus decora   **showy mountain-ash**   T N IR
    wooded dunes, especially near Lake Superior; moist mixed
    forests; white flowers in large flat-topped clusters; fruit bright
    red, relished by birds

Spiraea alba   **meadowsweet**   S N IR
    ✿   common shrub of wetlands; flowers white; to pale-pink in
    terminal clusters; leaves fine-toothed on yellow-brown stems

Waldsteinia fragarioides   **barren strawberry**   H N IR
    dry forests and thin, rocky soils; leaves shiny, flowers yellow

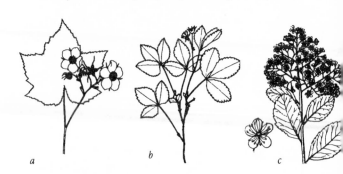

(a) Rubus parviflorus, (b) Rubus pubescens, (c) Spiraea alba

▶ *Fabaceae*   Pea or Bean Family

Amphicarpaea bracteata   **hog-peanut**   H I
    low vine of deciduous woods and swamps

Lathyrus latifolius   **everlasting pea**   H I
    disturbed places

Lathyrus maritimus   **beach pea**   H N IR
    ✿   sand dunes and beaches along Lake Superior; flowers purple-
    pink; divided leaves end in tendrils

Lathyrus ochroleucus   **white pea, pale vetchling**   H N IR
    mixed forests and forest openings

Lathyrus palustris   **marsh-pea**   H N
    swamps, wet meadows, marshes

Lathyrus pratensis   **meadow pea, yellow vetchling**   H I
    occasional escape from cultivation

Lathyrus sylvestris   **everlasting pea**   H I
    well-established European species

Lathyrus tuberosus   **tuberous vetchling**   H I
    occasional as an escape

Lathyrus venosus   **forest-pea**   H N
    sandy meadows and woods; rocky places

Lotus corniculata   **birdsfoot-trefoil**   H I
    planted and now established in fields and roadsides

Lupinus polyphyllus   lupine   H I
    native to western US; common near farms and along roads

Medicago lupulina   black medic   H I   IR
    aggressive weed of fields and disturbed areas

Medicago sativa   alfalfa   H I   IR
    crop plant established in meadows, roadsides, etc.

Melilotus alba   white sweet clover   H I   IR
    sand dunes; disturbed, usually calcium-rich soil

Melilotus officinalis   yellow sweet clover   H I   IR
    disturbed places

Robinia pseudoacacia   black locust   T I
    escaped from cultivation

Trifolium arvense   rabbitfoot clover   H I
    especially on sandy soil

Trifolium aureum   palmate hop-clover   H I   IR
    disturbed places and fields

Trifolium hybridum   alsike clover   H I   IR
    moist disturbed areas

Trifolium incarnatum   crimson clover   H I
    uncommon exotic of moist disturbed places

Trifolium pratense   red clover   H I   IR
    common along roads and in fields

Trifolium repens   white clover   H I   IR
    fields, roadsides, moist areas

Vicia americana   American vetch   H N   IR
  ❀ wide range of moist to dry habitats

Vicia cracca   bird-vetch   H I
    forming large matted patches in disturbed areas

Vicia sativa   common vetch   H I
    escape from cultivation

Vicia sepium   hedge-vetch   H I   IR
    uncommon along a trail on Isle Royale

Vicia villosa   hairy vetch   H I
    most common vetch in Michigan

(a) Lathyrus maritimus, (b) Vicia americana, (c) Shepherdia canadensis

▶*Eleagnaceae*   Oleaster Family

Shepherdia canadensis   rabbit-berry, soapberry   S N   IR
  ❀ shrub of mostly dry, sandy woods and wooded dunes; young
    leaves and twigs cinnamon brown, scurfy; fruit yellow-red,
    inedible

Lifeform codes: *T* (tree), *S* (shrub), *H* (herbaceous flowering plants), *G* (grasses and grass-like plants), *F* (ferns and fern-allies). Origin codes: *N* (native to Upper Peninsula), *I* (introduced species). Present on Isle Royale: *IR* (present), *blank* (absent). ❀ indicates an illustrated species.

▶ *Haloragaceae* — Water-milfoil Family

SC	*Myriophyllum alterniflorum*	water-milfoil	H	N	IR
	softwater lakes				
T	*Myriophyllum farwellii*	water-milfoil	H	N	
	uncommon in ponds and lakes				
	Myriophyllum heterophyllum	water-milfoil	H	N	
	lakes and rivers				
	Myriophyllum sibiricum	common water-milfoil	H	N	IR
	rivers, lakes, and ponds; often calcium-rich water				
	Myriophyllum tenellum	water-milfoil	H	N	IR
	common in softwater lakes; may form dense patches				
	Myriophyllum verticillatum	water-milfoil	H	N	IR
❀	lakes, ponds, rivers				

Myriophyllum verticillatum

▶ *Lythraceae* — Loosestrife Family

	Lythrum salicaria	purple loosestrife	H	I
	aggressive wetland weed; more common in lower Michigan; leaves opposite or 3-whorled; flowers pink to red-purple in leaf axils of upper stem			

▶ *Thymelaeaceae* — Mezereum Family

	Dirca palustris	leatherwood	S	N
❀	shrub of rich deciduous forests; pale yellow flowers appear in spring before leaves			

Dirca palustris

▶ *Onagraceae* — Evening-primrose Family

	Circaea alpina	alpine enchanter's nightshade	H	N	IR
❀	cedar swamps (common on rotting logs); hollows in deciduous forests				
	Epilobium angustifolium	fireweed	H	N	IR
❀	mostly dry habitats; abundant after fires; magenta flowers in long flowering stalk				

Status codes: *E* (endangered in Michigan), *T* (threatened in Michigan), *X* (extirpated from state), *SC* (special concern), *C2* (federal listing may be warranted but more information needed), *3C* (species once proposed for Federal listing but more abundant than previously believed).

Epilobium ciliatum   **American willow-herb**   H   N   IR
    wetlands; clearings in swamps

Epilobium coloratum   **eastern willow-herb**   H   N
    swamps and other wet places

Epilobium leptophyllum   **willow-herb**   H   N   IR
    sedge mats and meadows, swamps, wet clearings

SC *Epilobium palustre*   **marsh willow-herb**   H   N   IR
    sphagnum peatlands

Epilobium strictum   **northeastern willow-herb**   H   N
    swamps and fens; usually with sedges

Ludwigia palustris   **common water-purslane**   H   N
    shallow water; lake margins

Ludwigia polycarpa   **top-pod water-purslane**   H   N
    shallow water and margins

Oenothera biennis   **common evening-primrose**   H   N   IR
    ❀   dry sandy places; large yellow flowers open mostly one at a
    time, last for a single day

Oenothera fruticosa   **southern sundrops**   H   N   IR
    dry fields and clearings

Oenothera parviflora **small-flwrd evening-primrose**   H   N   IR
    sandy or rocky shores, dunes; mostly along Lake Superior

Oenothera perennis   **little sundrops**   H   N   IR
    moist sandy open areas, depressions in jack pine woods

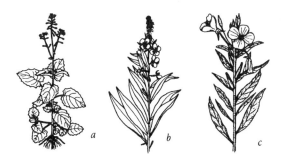

(a) Circaea alpina, (b) Epilobium angustifolium, (c) Oenothera biennis

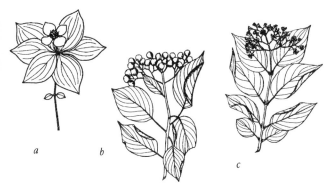

(a) Cornus canadensis, (b) Cornus alternifolia, (c) Cornus sericea

▶*Cornaceae*   Dogwood Family

Cornus alternifolia   **pagoda-dogwood**   S   N   IR
    ❀   deciduous and mixed forests, cedar swamps; branches and
    twigs green, grow horizontally; leaves alternate; fruit dark blue
    on red stem

Cornus canadensis   **bunchberry**   S   N   IR
❀   acidic conifer and mixed forests; cedar swamps; low shrub up to
    12 inches tall; forming patches; flowers cream-colored; fruit
    bright red
Cornus rugosa   **round-leaved dogwood** S   N   IR
    moist deciduous and mixed forests
Cornus sericea   **red osier-dogwood**   S   N   IR
❀   wetlands, sand dunes, rocky areas; stems reddish; flowers and
    fruit white; leaves opposite; also known as *Cornus stolonifera*

▶*Santalaceae*   Sandalwood Family

Comandra umbellata   **bastard toadflax**   H   N   IR
    sandy, gravelly, or rocky soil; dunes; partially parasitic on roots
    of other plants
Geocaulon lividum   **bastard toadflax**   H   N   IR
    dunes and rocky areas; parasitic on tree roots

▶*Viscaceae*   Christmas-mistletoe Family

Arceuthobium pusillum   **eastern dwarf mistletoe** H   N
    parasitic on branches of black spruce, sometimes on white
    spruce

▶*Celastraceae*   Staff-tree Family

Celastrus scandens   **American bittersweet** S   N
    vine with attractive orange berries

▶*Aquifoliaceae*   Holly Family

Ilex verticillata   **winterberry, Michigan holly** S   N
❀   peatlands; lake margins; leaves with prominent, slightly hairy
    veins; fruit bright scarlet, persistent
Nemopanthus mucronatus   **common mtn.-holly** S   N   IR
❀   tall shrub zone on fen margins; swamps and hollows; leaves
    dull green with abrupt sharp tip; fruit dull red

(a) Ilex verticillata, (b) Nemopanthus mucronatus

►*Euphorbiaceae*   Spurge Family

Euphorbia cyparissias   **cypress-spurge**   H   I   IR
     escaping ornamental ground cover

Euphorbia esula   **leafy spurge**   H   I
     aggressively spreading weed; more common in lower Michigan

Euphorbia glyptosperma   **ridge-seed spurge**   H   N/I
     recently disturbed areas; low mat-former

Euphorbia maculata   **spotted spurge**   H   I
     weed of lawn and garden; disturbed places

Euphorbia marginata   **snow-on-the-mountain**   H   I
     ornamental ground cover, sometimes escaping

Euphorbia peplus   **petty spurge**   H   I
     small uncommon weed of yards

Euphorbia serpyllifolia   **thyme-leaved spurge**   H   I   IR
     uncommon; native to western North America

►*Rhamnaceae*   Buckthorn Family

Ceanothus americanus   **New Jersey tea**   S   N
     dry sandy woodlands and fields; shrubs with red taproot,
     brown-green- stems; flowers white in dense terminal clusters

Ceanothus herbaceous   **prairie-redroot**   S   N   IR
     jack pine woods; rock outcrops

T   ***Ceanothus sanguineus***   **redstem ceanothus**   S   N
  ❀   widespread in Pacific Northwest; in Michigan known only from
     rocky woods in Keweenaw County near Brockway Mountain and
     Lake Bailey; stems red-purple

Rhamnus alnifolia   **American alder-buckthorn**   S   N   IR
  ❀   thicket-forming in cedar and tamarack swamps; alkaline sedge
     fens; leaves shiny with prominent veins; fruit small black
     berries

(a) Ceanothus sanguineus, (b) Rhamnus alnifolia

►*Vitaceae*   Grape Family

Parthenocissus vitacea   **Virginia creeper**   S   N
     rocky outcrops and woods; moist forests

Lifeform codes: *T* (tree), *S* (shrub), *H* (herbaceous flowering plants), *G* (grasses and grass-like plants), *F* (ferns and fern-allies). Origin codes: *N* (native to Upper Peninsula), *I* (introduced species). Present on Isle Royale: *IR* (present), *blank* (absent). ❀ indicates an illustrated species.

►*Linaceae*   Flax Family

Linum catharticum   **white flax**   H I
    locally naturalized
Linum usitatissimum   **common flax**   H I
    uncommon as a garden escape

►*Polygalaceae*   Milkwort Family

Polygala paucifolia   **fringed polygala**   H N IR
❀   mixed and conifer forests; sandy or rocky beach ridges; leaves
    few, near top of stem, bright green and glossy, persist in
    winter; flowers magenta-pink

Polygala paucifolia

Polygala sanguinea   **blood-milkwort**   H N
    sandy meadows; marsh edges
Polygala vulgaris   **polygala**   H I
    uncommon garden escape

►*Aceraceae*   Maple Family

Acer negundo   **box-elder**   T N
    moist alluvial soil; disturbed areas
Acer pensylvanicum   **striped maple**   S N
❀   moist deciduous and mixed forests; cedar swamps; bark smooth
    with green or red stripes; leaves with 3 lobes and small sharp
    teeth
Acer platanoides   **Norway-maple**   T I
    sometimes escaping shade tree
Acer rubrum   **red maple**   T N IR
❀   common tree of dry to swampy woods; readily sprouts after
    clearing; branches smooth and light gray, twigs red; leaves with
    large sharp teeth
Acer saccharinum   **silver-maple, soft maple** T N
    swamp and alluvial forests
Acer saccharum   **sugar maple**   T N IR
❀   characteristic tree of upland forests; leaves with rounded lobes
    and pointed tips; twigs brown
Acer spicatum   **mountain-maple**   S N IR
❀   mixed and conifer forests; sometimes in conifer swamps; young
    branches red hairy; leaves hairy below with large blunt teeth;
    fruit red and persistent

Status codes: *E* (endangered in Michigan), *T* (threatened in Michigan), *X* (extirpated from state),
SC (special concern), *C2* (federal listing may be warranted but more information needed), *3C*
(species once proposed for Federal listing but more abundant than previously believed).

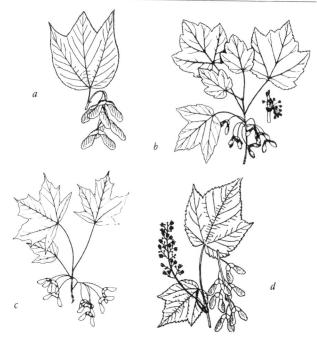

(a) Acer pensylvanicum, (b) Acer rubrum, (c) Acer saccharum, (d) Acer spicatum

▶*Anacardiaceae*   Cashew Family

Rhus glabra   **smooth sumac**   S   N
❀   fields and openings; rocky places

Rhus glabra

Rhus typhina   **staghorn-sumac**   S   N   IR
  fields and rocky openings

Toxicodendron radicans   **common poison-ivy**   S   N   IR
  sandy and rocky areas; shrubby growth form in U.P.

▶*Oxalidaceae*   Wood sorrel Family

Oxalis acetosella   **northern wood-sorrel** H   N   IR
  mixed forests; *Oxalis* leaves three-parted, somewhat similar to
  clover leaves

Oxalis stricta   **common yellow wood-sorrel** H   N
  usually in dry sandy fields and disturbed places

Lifeform codes: *T* (tree), *S* (shrub), *H* (herbaceous flowering plants), *G* (grasses and grass-like plants), *F* (ferns and fern-allies). Origin codes: *N* (native to Upper Peninsula), *I* (introduced species). Present on Isle Royale: *IR* (present), *blank* (absent). ❀ indicates an illustrated species.

►*Geraniaceae* — Geranium Family

Erodium cicutarium   **redstem-filaree, stork's bill**   H   I
> weed of dry, sandy or rocky places

Geranium bicknellii   **wild geranium**   H N IR
> ✿ rock outcrops and dry coarse soil

Geranium carolinianum   **Carolina crane's-bill**   H N IR
> dry, sandy or rocky openings

Geranium maculatum   **wild geranium**   H I
> moist deciduous woods; hollows and streambanks

Geranium pusillum   **small-flowered crane's-bill**   H I
> dry disturbed areas

Geranium robertianum   **herb-Robert**   H I
> rich deciduous forests and clearings

►*Balsaminaceae* — Touch-me-not Family

Impatiens capensis   **orange touch-me-not**   H N IR
> swamps; disturbed wetlands; flowers yellow-orange with red spots;
> capsule explodes when ripe

(a) Geranium bicknellii, (b) Aralia hispida, (c) Aralia nudicaulis,
(d) Oplopanax horridus

►*Araliaceae* — Ginseng Family

Aralia hispida   **bristly sarsaparilla**   S N IR
> ✿ dry, sandy woods, dunes and disturbed areas; may form large
> colonies; plants with spiny stems; flowers at end of leafybranches

Aralia nudicaulis   **wild sarsaparilla**   H N IR
> ✿ moist forests, swamps, and wooded dunes; flowers greenish
> white on naked stalk below leaves; fruit dark purple

Aralia racemosa   **spikenard**   H N IR
> moist deciduous and mixed forests near clearings; cedar
> swamps; many flowers at end of leafy stems

Status codes: *E* (endangered in Michigan), *T* (threatened in Michigan), *X* (extirpated from state), *SC* (special concern), *C2* (federal listing may be warranted but more information needed), *3C* (species once proposed for Federal listing but more abundant than previously believed).

T *Oplopanax horridus*   **devil's club**   S N IR
❖ plant of Pacific Northwest; in Michigan, known only from moist
  woods on Isle Royale; plants with strong thorns

 Panax trifolius   **dwarf ginseng**   H N
  moist to wet deciduous or hemlock forests

►*Apiaceae*   Carrot Family

Aegopodium podagraria   **goutweed**   H I
 garden escape

Carum carvi   **caraway**   H I IR
 established in fields and waste places

Cicuta bulbifera   **bulbiferous water-hemlock** H N IR
 marshy areas, tamarack swamps; toxic if eaten; small bulblets
 develop in leaf axils

Conium maculatum   **poison hemlock**   H I
 roadsides, fields, and banks; entire plant toxic; plants with
 unpleasant odor, white flower clusters, spotted stems and lacy
 parsley-like leaves

Cryptotaenia canadensis   **honewort**   H N
 rich deciduous forests and swamps

Daucus carota   **Queen Anne's lace**   H I
 common weed of disturbed areas

Heracleum lanatum   **cow-parsnip**   H N IR
❖ low areas and moist forest openings; robust plant to 8 feet tall
  with large maple-like leaves; topped by clusters of white
  flowers

Osmorhiza chilensis   **tapering sweet cicely**   H N IR
 deciduous, mixed, and conifer forests; *Osmorhiza* plants are
 aromatic with leaves parted into threes several times

Osmorhiza claytonii   **bland sweet cicely**   H N IR
❖ deciduous and mixed forests

SC *Osmorhiza depauperata*   **blunt sweet cicely**   H N IR
 uncommon; mixed forests

Osmorhiza longistylis   **long-styled sweet cicely** H N
 rich, moist to swampy deciduous forests

Pastinaca sativa   **parsnip**   H I IR
 established exotic of fields and roadsides

Petroselinum crispum   **parsley**   H I
 rarely escaping garden plant

Sanicula marilandica   **black snakeroot**   H N IR
 deciduous and mixed forests; cedar swamps

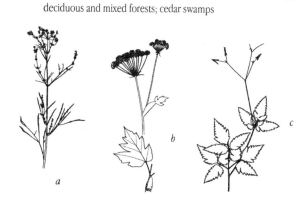

(a) Cicuta bulbifera, (b) Heracleum lanatum, (c) Osmorhiza chilensis

Sium suave   **water-parsnip**   H N IR
- ❋   marshes, potholes, and shallow water; distinguished from hemlocks by its ribbed stem and once pinnate leaves with narrow, toothed leaflets; may be toxic

Taenidia integerrima   **yellow-pimpernel**   H N
    jack pine woods; sandy areas and dunes

Zizia aurea   **common golden alexanders** H N
    swamps and fens; streambanks; flowers yellow in branched terminal clusters; leaves divided into 3 leaflets

▶ *Gentianaceae*   Gentian Family

T *Gentiana linearis*   **narrow-leaved gentian** H N
    acidic swamps and wet places; herb with narrow, opposite, clasping leaves; flowers violet-blue

Gentiana rubricaulis   **Great Lakes gentian** H N IR
    wetland margins and swales

Halenia deflexa   **halenia**   H N IR
    moist forests and peatlands

(a) Sium suave, (b) Apocynum androsaemifolium

▶ *Apocynaceae*   Dogbane Family

Apocynum androsaemifolium **spreading dogbane** H N IR
- ❋   dry sandy or rocky openings; leaves in pairs along spreading branches; flowers pink, bell-shaped; plants with milky juice

Vinca minor   **periwinkle**   H I
    planted as ground cover; occasionally escaping

▶ *Asclepiadaceae*   Milkweed Family

Asclepias syriaca   **common milkweed** H N
    roadsides and fields; flowers rose or brown-purple, in clusters in leaf axils

▶ *Solanaceae*   Nightshade Family

Leucophysalis grandiflora **white-fl. ground-cherry** H N IR
    dry sandy or rocky places

▶*Convolvulaceae*   Morning-glory Family

Calystegia sepium   **hedge-bindweed**   H N/I   IR
   moist meadows and disturbed areas
Calystegia spithamaea   **low bindweed**   H N   IR
   dry rocky or sandy soil
Convolvulus arvensis   **field-bindweed**   H I
   twining weed of fields and waste places

▶*Menyanthaceae*   Buckbean Family

Menyanthes trifoliata   **bog buckbean**   H N   IR
  ❀ pools in fens and swamps; leaves and flower stalk upright from
   rhizome; leaves with 3 leaflets; flowers white, 5 lobed; fruit
   round and green

Menyanthes trifoliata

▶*Polemoniaceae*   Phlox Family

Phlox paniculata   **summer-phlox**   H I
   garden escape on rich, moist soil
Phlox subulata   **moss-pink**   H I
   garden escape; sandy and rocky areas

▶*Hydrophyllaceae*   Waterleaf Family

T   **Phacelia franklinii**   **Canadian phacelia**   H N   IR
   open places in woods and rocks

▶*Boraginaceae*   Borage Family

Borago officinalis   **borage**   H I
   garden escape
Cynoglossum officinale   **hound's tongue**   H I   IR
   weed of disturbed places
Cynoglossum virginianum   **wild comfrey**   H N   IR
   jack pine woods and rocky openings
Hackelia virginiana   **stickseed**   H N
   upland woods
Lappula squarrosa   **two-row stickseed**   H I   IR
   weed of waste places

Lifeform codes: *T* (tree), *S* (shrub), *H* (herbaceous flowering plants), *G* (grasses and grass-like plants), *F* (ferns and fern-allies). Origin codes: *N* (native to Upper Peninsula), *I* (introduced species). Present on Isle Royale: *IR* (present), *blank* (absent). ❀ indicates an illustrated species.

Mertensia paniculata   **northern bluebell**   H N   IR
   ✿   moist open forests and wetland margins

Myosotis laxa   **smaller forget-me-not** H N
    moist soil and shallow water

Myosotis scorpioides   **water scorpion-grass**   H I   IR
    wet soil and shallow water

Myosotis sylvatica   **garden forget-me-not**   H I   IR
    Isle Royale; garden escape

Myosotis verna   **early scorpion grass**   H N
    upland woods and fields

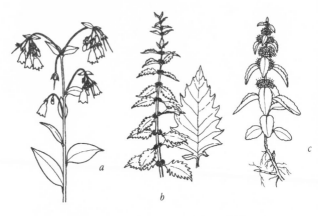

(a) *Mertensia paniculata*, (b) *Lycopus americanus*, (c) *Mentha arvensis*

►*Verbenaceae*   Vervain Family

Verbena bracteata   **prostrate vervain**   H I
    fields and waste places

►*Lamiaceae*   Mint Family

Dracocephalum parviflorum   **Amer. dragon-head**   H N   IR
    dry rocky openings

Galeopsis tetrahit   **hemp-nettle**   H I   IR
    sandy, often disturbed sites

Glechoma hederacea   **ground-ivy**   H I   IR
    moist woods, streambanks, and openings

Lycopus americanus   **Amer. water-horehound** H N   IR
   ✿   swamps, marshes, and streambanks; small white flowers in
    clusters in leaf axils

Lycopus uniflorus   **n. water-horehound**   H N   IR
    swamps and sometimes fens; leaves coarsely toothed; flowers
    white in small dense whorls in leaf axils

Mentha arvensis   **field-mint**   H N   IR
   ✿   swamps, marshes, banks; aromatic plants with white or pink-
    violet flowers in axils

Mentha spicata   **spearmint**   H I
    escape of moist places; streambanks

Mentha x *piperita*   **peppermint**   H I
    occasionally established in moist areas

Nepeta cataria   **catnip**   H I
    occasional on disturbed sites

Status codes: *E* (endangered in Michigan), *T* (threatened in Michigan), *X* (extirpated from state), *SC* (special concern), *C2* (federal listing may be warranted but more information needed), *3C* (species once proposed for Federal listing but more abundant than previously believed).

Physostegia virginiana   **obedience**   H I
> escape into moist woods or openings; flowers pink and showy, remain in position if pushed

Prunella vulgaris   **self-heal**   H N/I   IR
> ❀ forest openings and trails; leaves usually hairy; hood of flower violet, pale lower lip

Satureja vulgaris   **wild basil**   H N   IR
> dry woods, openings and disturbed places; leaves soft hairy; flowers deep pink, clustered from leaf axils

Scutellaria galericulata   **marsh-skullcap**   H N   IR
> ❀ pond and lake margins; streambanks; solitary blue flowers one inch long in upper leaf axils

Scutellaria lateriflora   **skullcap**   H N   IR
> lakeshores, wet forests; small blue flowers in long clusters from leaf axils

Stachys palustris   **hedge-nettle**   H N   IR
> moist or wet places

Thymus marchallianous   **thyme**   H I   IR
> uncommon exotic in disturbed area, Isle Royale

Thymus pulegioides   **creeping thyme**   H I   IR
> uncommon exotic in disturbed rocky area, Isle Royale

(a) Prunella vulgaris, (b) Scutellaria galericulata, (c) Hippuris vulgaris

►*Hippuridaceae*   Mare's-tail Family

Hippuris vulgaris   **mare's tail**   H N   IR
> ❀ pond margins and shallow water

►*Callitrichaceae*   Water-starwort Family

SC *Callitriche hermaphroditica*   **water-starwort**   H N   IR
> ❀ shallow to deep water; lakes and streams

Callitriche hermaphroditica

Callitriche palustris   **water-starwort**   H N   IR
> shallow water and shores on sand or mud

SC *Littorella uniflora*   **American shore-grass**   H N
> submersed in shallow water

►*Plantaginaceae*   Plantain Family

Plantago altissima   **plantain**   H   I
    weed of waste places

Plantago lanceolata   **English plantain**   H   I
    weed of lawns and roadsides

Plantago major   **common plantain**   H   I   IR
    common weed of lawns and vacant lots

Plantago rugelii   **American plantain**   H   N
    weed of lawns and roadsides

►*Oleaceae*   Olive Family

Fraxinus americana   **white ash**   T   N
    ❀   rich, moist forests

Fraxinus americana

Fraxinus nigra   **black ash**   T   N   IR
    swamps and wet forests; tree with smooth gray bark, black
    buds; fruit single winged, grouped in long bunches

Fraxinus pennsylvanica   **green ash**   T   N
    swamps and wet forests

►*Scrophulariaceae*   Figwort Family

    Castilleja coccinea   **painted cup**   H   N
    moist meadows

T   **Castilleja septentrionalis**   **northeastern paintbrush**   H   N   IR
    rocky shores and openings; aspen groves

    Chelone glabra   **white turtlehead**   H   N   IR
    swamps; perennial with toothed, lance-shaped leaves up to 6
    inches long; flowers white and hooded at end of stems

T   **Collinsia parviflora**   **small blue-eyed Mary**   H   N   IR
    ❀   rocky ridges (Brockway Mountain) and shorelines

T   **Euphrasia disjuncta**   **arctic eyebright**   H   N
    peatlands, streambanks

    Euphrasia hudsoniana   **eyebright**   H   N   IR
    rocky shorelines on Isle Royale

    Euphrasia officinalis   **European eyebright**   H   I   IR
    Isle Royale; rocky shores, disturbed areas

    Linaria vulgaris   **butter-and-eggs**   H   I   IR
    established in fields and waste places

    Melampyrum lineare   **cow-wheat**   H   N   IR
    ❀   moist forests, peatlands, and rocky clearings; annual with white,
    yellow-tipped flowers; opposite leaves

Status codes: E (endangered in Michigan), *T* (threatened in Michigan), *X* (extirpated from state),
SC (special concern), *C2* (federal listing may be warranted but more information needed), *3C*
(species once proposed for Federal listing but more abundant than previously believed).

Mimulus moschatus   **musky monkey-flower** H   N/I
　　　near springs and creeks

Mimulus ringens   **Allegheny monkey-flower** H   N   IR
　　　swamps; blue flowers on long stalks in upper leaf axils

Pedicularis canadensis   **wood-betony**   H   N
　　　upland woods and openings

Scrophularia lanceolata   **American figwort**   H   N   IR
　　　open woods, openings

Verbascum thapsus   **common mullein**   H   I   IR
　　　dry rocky areas, roadsides

Veronica americana   **American speedwell**   H   N   IR
　❀　succulent trailing plant of swamps and streambanks; flowers
　　　blue

Veronica anagallis-aquatica **water-speedwell**   H   I
　❀　emergent in slow-moving streams; swamps; flowers blue-violet, in
　　　long clusters from upper leaf axils

Veronica arvensis   **corn-speedwell**   H   I   IR
　　　disturbed areas and grain fields; small blue flowers in leaf axils

Veronica chamaedrys   **Germander-speedwell** H   I
　　　weed of lawns and open places; flowers blue in long clusters

Veronica officinalis   **common speedwell**   H   I   IR
　　　dry woods and fields; stems trailing and hairy; flowers blue or
　　　lavender

Veronica peregrina   **purslane-speedwell**   H   N   IR
　　　old collection from island off Isle Royale

Veronica serpyllifolia   **thyme-leaved speedwell** H   I   IR
　　　widespread in fields and open areas; flowers white or pale blue

Veronica verna   **speedwell**   H   I   IR
　　　roadsides, other disturbed places

Veronicastrum virginicum   **Culver's root**   H   N   IR
　　　Isle Royale; moist to dry forests

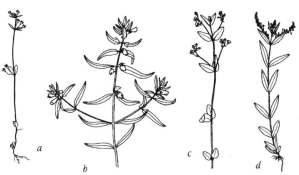

(a) Collinsia parviflora, (b) Melampyrum lineare, (c) Veronica americana,
(d) Veronica anagallis-aquatica

▶*Orobanchaceae*   Broom-rape Family

Conopholis americana   **squaw-root**   H   N
　　　rich forests; parasitic on oaks; stubby plants to 8 inches high;
　　　leaves scale-like and brownish; flowers yellowish, crowded on
　　　upper part of stem

►*Lentibulariaceae*   Bladderwort Family

SC ***Pinguicula vulgaris***   **violet butterwort**   H N IR
    ❀   moist rocky shorelines; fens; distinctive insectivorous plants; rosette of soft sticky leaves trap insects; basal leaves yellow-green; flowers single, violet on leafless stalk

Utricularia cornuta   **naked bladderwort**   H N IR
    shallow water, fens, and muddy shorelines

Utricularia gibba   **creeping bladderwort**   H N IR
    Isle Royale; shallow water of ponds and lakes

Utricularia intermedia   **northern bladderwort**   H N IR
    ❀   Isle Royale; shallow water of lakes and peatlands

Utricularia minor   **lesser bladderwort**   H N IR
    ❀   Isle Royale; shallow water of lakes and ponds

Utricularia vulgaris   **common bladderwort**   H N IR
    ❀   shallow water of lakes and ponds; our largest bladderwort; plants named for underwater sacs which open and close to trap aquatic insects; small yellow flowers raised on stalks above water surface.

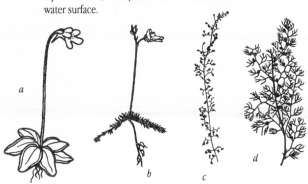

(a) Pinguicula vulgaris, (b) Utricularia intermedia, (c) U. minor, (d) U. vulgaris

►*Campanulaceae*   Bellflower Family

Campanula aparinoides   **marsh-bellflower**   H N IR
    margins of lakes and wetlands; leaves linear; stems slender and 3-angled; flowers pale blue to white

Campanula rapunculoides   **rover bellflower**   H I
    persistent weed of lawns and roadsides

Campanula rotundifolia   **harebell**   H N IR
    ❀   rocky shorelines and openings inland; flowers blue and bell-shaped, drooping

Lobelia dortmanna   **water-lobelia**   H N IR
    shallow water and pond margins; plants form rosette of fleshy hollow leaves rooted in sandy sediments; flowers raised above water

Campanula rotundifolia

Status codes: *E* (endangered in Michigan), *T* (threatened in Michigan), *X* (extirpated from state), *SC* (special concern), *C2* (federal listing may be warranted but more information needed), *3C* (species once proposed for Federal listing but more abundant than previously believed).

Lobelia kalmii　　　　　　　**lobelia**　　　　H　N　IR
　　rocky shorelines; peatlands
Lobelia spicata　　　　　　　**spiked lobelia**　　H　N
　　various habitats, often weedy

▶ *Rubiaceae*　　　　　　　Madder Family

Galium aparine　　　　　　**cleavers**　　　　　H　N
　❀　damp, shaded ground
Galium asprellum　　　　　　**rough bedstraw**　　H　N　IR
　　swamps and wet woods; stems bristly; leaves in whorls of 6;
　　small white flowers
Galium boreale　　　　　　**northern bedstraw**　H　N　IR
　❀　moist, sometimes rocky habitats; small white flowers in dense
　　clusters
Galium obtusum　　　　　　**bluntleaf-bedstraw**　H　N
　　swamps and wet meadows
Galium tinctorium　　　　　**s. three-lobed bedstraw** H　N　IR
　　sedge mats
Galium trifidum　　　　　　**n. three-lobed bedstraw** H　N　IR
　　swamps and streambanks
Galium triflorum　　　　　**sweet-scented bedstraw** H　N　IR
　❀　moist forests, occasionally swamps; leaves in whorls of 6
Mitchella repens　　　　　　**partridge-berry**　　H　N
　❀　moist to fairly dry woods; mat forming; leaves evergreen, shiny
　　with prominent veins; white flowers in pairs, joined; fruit
　　bright red double berries

(a) Galium aparine, (b) G. boreale, (c) G. triflorum, (d) Mitchella repens

▶ *Caprifoliaceae*　　　　　Honeysuckle Family

Diervilla lonicera　　　　　**bush-honeysuckle**　　S　N　IR
　❀　small shrub common along rock shorelines and openings;
　　rocky and sandy woods
Linnaea borealis　　　　　　**twinflower**　　　　S　N　IR
　❀　moist deciduous and mixed forests; hummocks in swamps;
　　trailing somewhat woody plants; pink flowers in pairs
Lonicera caerulea　　　　　**waterberry**　　　　S　N　IR
　　swamps and wet woods
Lonicera canadensis　　　　**fly-honeysuckle**　　S　N　IR
　❀　conifer forests; jack pine woods; flowers green-yellow; berries
　　red, in pairs

Lifeform codes: *T* (tree), *S* (shrub), *H* (herbaceous flowering plants), *G* (grasses and grass-like
plants), *F* (ferns and fern-allies). Origin codes: *N* (native to Upper Peninsula), *I* (introduced species).
Present on Isle Royale: *IR* (present), *blank* (absent). ❀ indicates an illustrated species.

Lonicera dioica   **wild honeysuckle**   S   N   IR
moist forests; dunes

Lonicera hirsuta   **hairy honeysuckle**   S   N   IR
✺   swamps and pond margins

T   *Lonicera involucrata*   **bearberry-honeysuckle**   S   N   IR
rare in Michigan; moist to dry woods

Lonicera oblongifolia   **swamp fly-honeysuckle**   S   N   IR
✺   swamps and fens; flowers yellow; berries usually orange and in
pairs; leaves densely hairy on underside

Lonicera prolifera   **grape-honeysuckle**   S   N
moist to wet forests

Lonicera tartarica   **Tartarian honeysuckle**   S   I   IR
Isle Royale; escaped from cultivation

Sambucus canadensis   **common elder**   S   N
moist woods and openings; branches warty; fruit dark purple,
edible when ripe

Sambucus racemosa   **red-berried elder**   S   N   IR
moist forests, rocky openings; fruit bright red, inedible

Symphoricarpos albus   **snowberry**   S   N   IR
✺   dry or rocky openings

Symphoricarpos occidentalis   **wolfberry**   S   N
meadows and openings

Symphoricarpos orbiculatus   **coralberry**   S   N
dry or rocky soil; forest edges

T   *Viburnum edule*   **squashberry**   S   N/I   IR
✺   mixed and conifer forests; common on Isle Royale; fruits
orange-red; used for jellies after frost

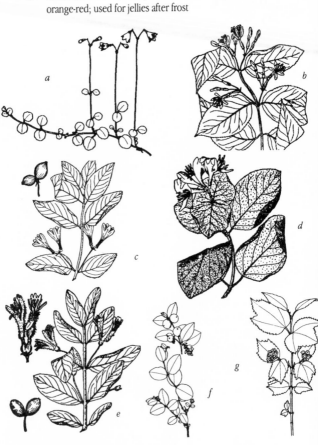

(a) *Linnaea borealis*, (b) *Diervilla lonicera*, (c) *Lonicera canadensis*,
(d) *L. hirsuta*, (e) *L. oblongifolia*, (f) *Symphoricarpos albus*, (g) *Viburnum edule*

Status codes: *E* (endangered in Michigan), *T* (threatened in Michigan), *X* (extirpated from state),
SC (special concern), *C2* (federal listing may be warranted but more information needed), *3C*
(species once proposed for Federal listing but more abundant than previously believed).

Viburnum opulus high-bush cranberry S N/I IR
    streambanks and lake margins; moist woods

Viburnum rafinesquianum downy arrow-wood S N
    dry, rocky woods

▶*Asteraceae* Aster Family

Achillea millefolium common yarrow H N/I IR
    common plant of openings and meadows; flowers white in flat-topped or rounded clusters

Adenocaulon bicolor trail-plant H N
    ❀ moist woods; disjunct in Keweenaw from western US

Ambrosia artemisiifolia common ragweed H N
    waste places

Ambrosia psilostachya western ragweed H N
    dry waste places

Ambrosia trifida giant ragweed H N
    moist disturbed areas

Anaphalis margaritacea pearly everlasting H N IR
    ❀ dry openings and outcrops; stems white woolly; leaves gray-green; often dried for flower arrangements

T ***Antennaria microphylla*** rosy pussytoes H N IR
    dry open woods and meadows

Antennaria neglecta field-pussytoes H N IR
    dry woods and openings; rocky shorelines

Antennaria plantaginifolia plantain pussytoes H N IR
    dry woods and rock openings

Anthemis arvensis corn-chamomile H I
    fields and waste places

Arctium lappa great burdock H I
    occasional along roads and disturbed areas

Arctium minus common burdock H I IR
    Isle Royale; disturbed places and roadsides

T ***Arnica cordifolia*** heart-leaved arnica H N
    ❀ dry forests; disjunct from western North America (sometimes considered *Arnica whitneyi*); Brockway Mountain

(a) Adenocaulon bicolor, (b) Anaphalis margaritacea, (c) Arnica cordifolia

Artemisia absinthinum common wormwood H I
    fields and waste places

Artemisia biennis biennial wormwood H I
    sandy areas, waste places

Artemisia campestris wormwood H N IR
    ❀ sandy open areas and dunes

Lifeform codes: *T* (tree), *S* (shrub), *H* (herbaceous flowering plants), *G* (grasses and grass-like plants), *F* (ferns and fern-allies). Origin codes: *N* (native to Upper Peninsula), *I* (introduced species). Present on Isle Royale: *IR* (present), *blank* (absent). ❀ indicates an illustrated species.

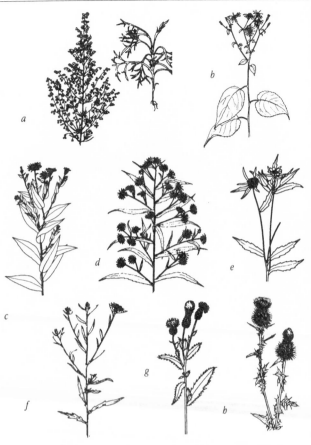

a) Artemisia campestris, (b) Aster macrophyllus, (c) Aster modestus,
(d) Aster puniceus, (e) Bidens cernua, (f) Centaurea jacea, (g) Cirsium arvense,
(b) Cirsium vulgare

(a) Erigeron acris, (b) Erigeron annuus, (c) Erigeron philadelphicus,
(d) Hieracium aurantiacum, (e) Eupatorium maculatum, (f) E. perfoliatum

Status codes: *E* (endangered in Michigan), *T* (threatened in Michigan), *X* (extirpated from state),
SC (special concern), *C2* (federal listing may be warranted but more information needed), *3C*
(species once proposed for Federal listing but more abundant than previously believed).

Artemisia ludoviciana	white sage	H	I	
dry open places				
Artemisia stelleriana	dusty miller	H	I	
escape; occasional near sandy beaches				
Aster ciliolatus	n. heart-leaved aster	H	N	IR
dry, rocky woods and clearings				
Aster firmus	shining aster	H	N	
moist woods and wetlands				
Aster lanceolatus	eastern lined-aster	H	N	IR
swamps and streambanks, sometimes weedy in fields; ray flowers white				
Aster lateriflorus	goblet-aster	H	N	IR
sandy woods and openings				
Aster macrophyllus	big-leaved aster	H	N	IR
❀ common plant of deciduous and mixed forests; plants with large heart-shaped leaves; usually without flowers				
Aster modestus	northwestern sticky aster	H	N	IR
❀ rocky shorelines and openings				
Aster prenanthoides	zigzag aster	H	N	
moist forests and streambanks				
Aster pubentior	nw. flat-topped white aster	H	N	
moist to wet forests				
Aster puniceus	bristly aster	H	N	IR
❀ swamps; near ponds and lakes; long, reddish hairy stems; flowers blue, pink or white				
Aster sagittifolius	arrow-leaved aster	H	N	
moist forests; streambanks				
Aster sericeus	western silvery aster	H	N	
dry meadows and openings				
Aster tradescanti	shore-aster	H	N	
rocky shorelines and lake margins				
Aster umbellatus	tall flat-topped white aster	H	N	IR
swamps; flowers white, in clusters at ends of upper stems				
Bidens beckii	water beggar-ticks	H	N	IR
submersed in lakes and streams				
Bidens cernua	bur-marigold	H	N	IR
❀ annual plant of swamps and fens; flower heads with 6-8 yellow rays; flowers nodding				
Bidens connata	purplestem beggar-ticks	H	N	
wet disturbed places				
Bidens coronata	n. tickseed-sunflower	H	N	
wetlands				
Centaurea cyanus	bachelor's button	H	I	IR
fields and waste places				
Centaurea dubia	short-fringed knapweed	H	I	
fields, roadsides and waste places				
Centaurea jacea	brown knapweed	H	I	
❀ fields, roadsides and waste places				
Centaurea maculosa	spotted knapweed	H	I	
fields, roadsides and waste places				
Centaurea nigra	black knapweed	H	I	
fields, roadsides and waste places				
Chrysanthemum balsamita	costmary	H	I	
occasional escape				
Chrysanthemum leucanthemum	ox-eye daisy	H	I	IR
fields, roadsides				
Chrysanthemum parthenium	feverfew	H	I	
occasional in waste places				

Cichorium intybus	chicory	H I	
weed of fields and waste places			
Cirsium arvense	Canada-thistle	H I	IR
❀ noxious weed of disturbed areas and fields			
Cirsium muticum	swamp-thistle	H N	IR
swamps, fens, wet meadows			
Cirsium palustre	marsh-thistle	H I	
introduced; woods			
Cirsium vulgare	bull-thistle	H I	IR
❀ weed of fields and waste places			
Conyza canadensis	horseweed	H N	IR
weed of old fields			
Crepis tectorum	hawk's beard	H I	IR
Isle Royale; uncommon, collected once			
Echinacea pallida	prairie coneflower	H I	
dry openings and fields			
Erigeron acris	trimorphic daisy	H N	
❀ meadows			
Erigeron annuus	annual fleabane	H N	IR
❀ rocky openings and fields, disturbed places			
Erigeron hyssopifolius	hyssop-daisy	H N	
rocky shorelines			
Erigeron philadelphicus	Philadelphia daisy	H N	IR
❀ moist meadows; plants long hairy; numerous pink-white flower rays surrounding yellow disk flowers			
Erigeron strigosus	rough fleabane	H N	IR
meadows and rocky ridges and openings			
Eupatorium maculatum	spotted joe-pye weed	H N	IR
❀ meadows and fields; large upright plant with whorled leaves; flowers pink-purple			
Eupatorium perfoliatum	boneset	H N	
❀ moist meadows and wetland margins; white flowers; opposite leaves joined at base			
Euthamia graminifolia	flat-topped goldenrod	H N	IR
moist meadows and open wetlands			
Gnaphalium macounii	clammy cudweed	H N	IR
old fields and waste places			
Gnaphalium uliginosum	low cudweed	H I	
weed of streambanks and meadows, wet or dry			
Helianthus giganteus	swamp-sunflower	H I	
swamps and wet meadows			
Helianthus maximilianii	Maximilian-sunflower	H I	
sandy openings			
Helianthus x laetiflorus	sunflower	H I	
escape along roadsides			
Heliopsis helianthoides	sunflower-everlasting	H N	
woods, fields, and waste places			
Hieracium aurantiacum	orange king-devil	H I	IR
❀ attractive but aggressive orange-flowered weed of old fields, lawns and openings			
Hieracium kalmii	Canada hawkweed	H N	IR
open sandy places and dunes			
Hieracium piloselloides	glaucous king-devil	H I	IR
weed of roadsides and fields; dunes			
Hieracium scabrum	sticky hawkweed	H N	IR
dry sandy woods and fields; stems red and bristly; leaves with glandular margins; flowers yellow			
Hieracium umbellatum	northern hawkweed	H N	IR
open woods and dunes			

Status codes: *E* (endangered in Michigan), *T* (threatened in Michigan), *X* (extirpated from state), *SC* (special concern), *C2* (federal listing may be warranted but more information needed), *3C* (species once proposed for Federal listing but more abundant than previously believed).

Krigia biflora **orange dwarf dandelion** H N
    woods and fields

Lactuca biennis **tall blue lettuce** H N IR
    robust biennial with milky sap and blue-rayed flowers; moist
    forest openings and near wetlands

Lactuca canadensis **tall lettuce** H N IR
    open woods and fields; flowers with pale yellow rays

T *Lactuca pulchella* **blue lettuce** H N IR
    moist meadows and openings

Lapsana communis **nipplewort** H I
    fields and disturbed places

Liatris cylindracea **few-headed blazing star** H N
    dry fields

Liatris scariosa **northern blazing star** H I
    dry open places

Matricaria maritima **scentless chamomile** H I IR
    Isle Royale; rocky beaches

Matricaria matricarioides **pineapple-weed** H I IR
    clearings and disturbed places; small yellow flowers; plants with
    pineapple odor

Matricaria recutita **chamomile** H I
    roadsides and waste places

Petasites frigidus **n. sweet coltsfoot** H N IR
    ❀ swamps and moist meadows

Prenanthes alba **rattlesnake-root** H N IR
    conifer forests and swamps; plants with milky sap

Prenanthes racemosa **glaucous white lettuce** H N IR
    rocky shorelines and openings; plants with milky sap

Ratibida pinnata **globular coneflower** H I
    dry woods and fields

Rudbeckia hirta **black-eyed Susan** H N IR
    ❀ familiar plant of fields and clearings; flowers single; ray flowers
    yellow, disk flowers purple-brown

Senecio aureus **heart-leaved groundsel** H N
    moist woods and swamps

T *Senecio indecorus* **taller discoid groundsel** H N IR
    dry rocky openings

Senecio pauperculus **n.meadow-groundsel** H N IR
    ❀ rocky shores and openings, meadows; yellow flowers; leaves
    small and few near top of stem

Senecio sylvaticus **woodland-groundsel** H I
    weed of disturbed places

(a) Lactuca biennis, (b) Petasites frigidus, (c) Rudbeckia hirta,
(d) Senecio pauperculus

Solidago bicolor   **silver-rod**   H N
  ❁ dry woods and sandy-rocky openings; ray flowers silvery white
Solidago canadensis   **common goldenrod**   H N IR
  ❁ familiar yellow-flowered plants of openings and recent burns;
      leaves with 3 large parallel veins
SC ***Solidago canadensis* var. *subserrata*** **w. goldenrod** H N
      woods and meadow; *Solidago lepida* in some floras
SC ***Solidago decumbens***   **reclining goldenrod**   H N
      boreal species barely entering our range
Solidago flexicaulis   **zigzag goldenrod**   H N
      woods; upper part of stem bent slightly at leaf axil
Solidago gigantea   **smooth goldenrod**   H N IR
      moist meadows
Solidago bispida   **hairy goldenrod**   H N IR
  ❁ rocky shores and ridges; hairy leaves becoming smaller near
      top of plant
Solidago juncea   **early goldenrod**   H N IR
      sandy or rocky openings
Solidago nemoralis   **gray goldenrod**   H N IR
  ❁ dry, rocky openings
Solidago ptarmicoides   **goldenrod**   H N IR
      common along rocky shores
Solidago rugosa   **wrinkle-leaved goldenrod** H N
      moist woods and openings
Solidago simplex   **goldenrod**   H N IR
  ❁ rocky openings and shorelines
Solidago speciosa   **showy goldenrod**   H N
      dry rocky woods and ridges
Solidago uliginosa   **n. bog-goldenrod**   H N IR
  ❁ swamps and fens; flowers mostly on one side of stem

(a) Solidago bicolor, (b) S. canadensis, (c) S. bispida,
(d) S. nemoralis, (e) S. simplex, (f) S. uliginosa

Sonchus arvensis   **perennial sow-thistle** H I IR
      weed of disturbed areas and clearings
Sonchus asper   **prickly sow-thistle**   H I
      weed of disturbed areas

Status codes: *E* (endangered in Michigan), *T* (threatened in Michigan), *X* (extirpated from state), *SC* (special concern), *C2* (federal listing may be warranted but more information needed), *3C* (species once proposed for Federal listing but more abundant than previously believed).

Sonchus oleraceus **common sow-thistle** H I
    weed of disturbed areas; leaves clasping and spiny toothed

Tanacetum vulgare **common tansy** H I IR
    fields, roadsides and waste places

Taraxacum laevigatum **red-seeded dandelion** H I
    fields and disturbed places; much less common than
    Taraxacum officinale

Taraxacum officinale **common dandelion** H I IR
    lawns, fields, disturbed places; common

Tragopogon dubius **fistulous goat's-beard** H I
    dry fields and openings

Tragopogon porrifolius **salsify** H I
    moist clearings and roadsides

Tragopogon pratensis **showy goat's-beard** H I IR
    moist fields and waste places

►*Alismataceae*   Water-Plantain Family

Alisma triviale **water-plantain** H N
    ❀   shallow water and wet places; flowers small, white or pinkish

Sagittaria cuneata **northern arrowhead** H N IR
    ❀   Isle Royale; plants emergent from shallow water and on wet
    shores; leaves variable; flowers white, usually in whorls of
    three; seeds and tubers eaten by waterfowl

Sagittaria graminea **grass-leaved sagittaria** H N IR
    shallow water and muddy shores; large tubers eaten by muskrat

Sagittaria latifolia **wapato, duck-potato** H N IR
    ❀   shallow water, shores, marshes; tubers eaten by waterfowl and
    muskrat

Sagittaria rigida **sessile-fruited arrowhead** H N
    shallow water, shores, marshes

(a) Alisma triviale, (b) Sagittaria cuneata, (c) Sagittaria latifolia

►*Hydrocharitaceae*   Frog's-bit Family

Elodea canadensis **common waterweed** H N IR
    shallow to deep water

Elodea nuttallii **free-flowered waterweed** H N
    shallow to deep water; less common than *Elodea canadensis*

Vallisneria americana **tape-grass, water-celery** H N IR
    shallow to deep water; leaves in a tuft, long and ribbon-like;
    tips often floating on surface

---

feform codes: *T* (tree), *S* (shrub), *H* (herbaceous flowering plants), *G* (grasses and grass-like
lants), *F* (ferns and fern-allies). Origin codes: *N* (native to Upper Peninsula), *I* (introduced species).
esent on Isle Royale: *IR* (present), *blank* (absent). ❀ indicates an illustrated species.

► *Scheuchzeriaceae*   Scheuchzeria Family

Scheuchzeria palustris   **pod-grass**   H   N   IR
- ✱   wet places in fens

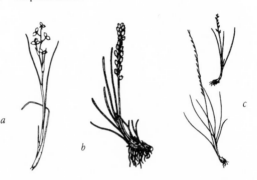

(a) Scheuchzeria palustris, (b) Triglochin maritimum, (c) Triglochin palustre

► *Juncaginaceae*   Arrow-grass Family

Triglochin maritimum   **common arrow-grass**   H   N   IR
- ✱   wet places along shores, marshes, fens; alkali tolerant

Triglochin palustre   **arrow-grass**   H   N
- ✱   wet sandy shores and marshes; wet places in open peatlands; alkali tolerant

► *Potamogetonaceae*   Pondweed Family

Potamogeton alpinus   **red pondweed**   H   N   IR
- ✱   shallow to deep, usually cold water; pondweeds very important for fish and birds

(a) Potamogeton alpinus, (b) P. epihydrus, (c) P. gramineus, (d) P. praelongus, (e) P. zosteriformis

Potamogeton amplifolius　　**bigleaf pondweed**　　H　N　IR
　　lakes, ponds, and rivers; flower cluster raised above water
　　surface; most pondweeds have submerged and floating leaves of
　　different shapes

Potamogeton epihydrus　　**ribbonleaf-pondweed**　　H　N　IR
❀　lakes, ponds, rivers

Potamogeton filiformis　　**threadleaf-pondweed**　　H　N　IR
　　lakes and rivers

Potamogeton foliosus　　**leafy pondweed**　　H　N　IR
　　shallow to deep water of lakes, ponds, and streams

Potamogeton friesii　　**Fries' pondweed**　　H　N
　　shallow to deep water of lakes, ponds, and streams

Potamogeton gramineus　　**variable pondweed**　　H　N　IR
❀　ponds and lakes

Potamogeton natans　　**floating pondweed**　　H　N　IR
　　usually shallow water of lakes, ponds, rivers

Potamogeton nodosus　　**longleaf pondweed**　　H　N
　　most common in rivers, sometimes in lakes; shallow water

Potamogeton obtusifolius　　**bluntleaf pondweed**　　H　N　IR
　　peatland pools, lakes, ponds, and streams

Potamogeton pectinatus　　**sago pondweed**　　H　N
　　common in lakes, ponds, and streams

Potamogeton praelongus　　**whitestem-pondweed**　　H　N　IR
❀　usually in lakes; often in deep water

Potamogeton pusillus　　**slender pondweed**　　H　N　IR
　　shallower waters of lakes and ponds

Potamogeton richardsonii　　**pondweed**　　H　N　IR
　　Lake Superior, inland lakes and streams

Potamogeton robbinsii　　**fern-pondweed**　　H　N　IR
　　lakes, ponds, rivers

Potamogeton spirillus　　**n. snailseed-pondweed**　H　N　IR
　　shallow, quiet water of lakes and ponds

Potamogeton strictifolius　　**straight-leaved pondweed**　H　N　IR
　　shallow water of lakes and ponds

Potamogeton zosteriformis　　**flatstem-pondweed**　　H　N　IR
❀　shallow to deep lakes and streams; no floating leaves

►*Najadaceae*　　　　Water-nymph Family

Najas flexilis　　**northern water-nymph**　　H　N　IR
❀　aquatic annual; very common; "occurs in nearly every pond and
　　lake in Michigan" (Voss); rivers and streams

Najas gracillima　　**slender water-nymph**　　H　N
　　shallow, usually soft water ponds and lakes; mucky bottoms

a　　　　　　　　　　　　　　　　　　*b*

(a) Najas flexilis, (b) Acorus calamus

►*Acoraceae*   Sweet Flag Family

Acorus calamus   **sweet-flag**   H   N
❋   open wetlands and streambanks

►*Araceae*   Arum Family

Arisaema triphyllum   **jack-in-the-pulpit**   H   N   IR
❋   hollows and near springs in moist forests; familiar flower is a
      spathe; fruit a cluster of scarlet berries; fruit eaten by birds and
      mammals

Calla palustris   **wild calla, water-arum** H   N   IR
❋   open fens and swamp openings; sometimes in shallow water;
      numerous tiny flowers in a dense cluster (spadix); fruit a
      cluster of small red berries

Symplocarpus foetidus   **skunk-cabbage**   H   N   IR
❋   wet places, fens and swamps; many small flesh-colored or
      purplish flowers crowded in a cluster, surrounded by a leafy
      spathe; leaves to 2 feet long

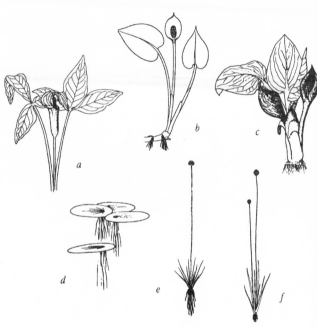

*(a) Arisaema triphyllum, (b) Calla palustris, (c) Symplocarpus foetidus,
(d) Lemna minor, (e) Xyris montana, (f) Eriocaulon aquaticum*

►*Lemnaceae*   Duckweed Family

Lemna minor   **lesser duckweed**   H   N
❋   quiet or stagnant water; may form large colonies at water
      surface

Lemna trisulca   **star-duckweed**   H   N   IR
      tangled masses below water surface

Spirodela polyrbiza   **greater duckweed**   H   N
      floating on surface of quiet waters; often with *Lemna minor*

►*Xyridaceae*   Yellow-eyed Grass Family

Xyris montana   **yellow-eyed-grass**   H   N
❀   wet places in shagnum peatlands; mucky shores

►*Eriocaulaceae*   Pipewort Family

Eriocaulon aquaticum   **pipewort**   H   N   IR
❀   pond and lake shorelines; plants submersed or exposed; soft,
       acidic water; also known as *Eriocaulon septangulare*

►*Juncaceae*   Rush Family

Juncus acuminatus   **rush**   G   N
       moist, usually sandy wetlands; not in peatlands
Juncus alpinoarticulatus   **rush**   G   N   IR
       wet sandy or gravelly shorelines; not in peatlands
Juncus arcticus   **wire-rush**   G   N
❀   sandy or gravelly wet places; low spots in dunes; also known as
       Juncus balticus
Juncus articulatus   **rush**   G   N
       wet places and shorelines; streams
Juncus brachycephalus   **rush**   G   N
       wet, sandy or marly shores; low spots on beaches
Juncus brevicaudatus   **rush**   G   N   IR
       wetlands (except peatlands); rocky shores
Juncus bufonius   **toad-rush**   G   N
       moist sandy areas; wet spots along trails and roadsides
Juncus canadensis   **rush**   G   N
       wet lake and pond margins; sand, mud, or peaty soil
Juncus effusus   **soft rush**   G   N   IR
❀   large tufted plants of wet meadows, marshes and clearings

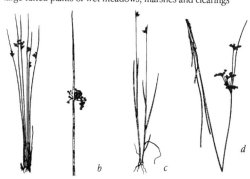

(a) Juncus arcticus, (b) Juncus effusus, (c) Juncus stygius, (d) Juncus tenuis

Juncus filiformis   **rush**   G   N   IR
       moist sand, gravel, or peaty soils
Juncus greenei   **rush**   G   N
       moist or dry sandy fields, dunes, and dune hollows
Juncus inflexus   **rush**   G   I
       introduced plant; in Michigan known only from ditch above
       Hancock

Lifeform codes: *T* (tree), *S* (shrub), *H* (herbaceous flowering plants), *G* (grasses and grass-like
plants), *F* (ferns and fern-allies). Origin codes: *N* (native to Upper Peninsula), *I* (introduced species).
Present on Isle Royale: *IR* (present), *blank* (absent). ❀ indicates an illustrated species.

Juncus marginatus	**rush**	G	N	

occasionally found in marshes and other moist sites

Juncus nodosus	**rush**	G	N	IR

wetlands, streambanks, ditches, wet borrow pits

Juncus pelocarpus	**rush**	G	N	IR

shores of soft water lakes and ponds

T   *Juncus stygius*   **rush**   G   N   IR

❀   rare in Michigan (Isle Royale only); more common northward

Juncus tenuis	**path-rush**	G	N	IR

❀   dry or moist, often compacted soil; roadsides, trails, clearings

Luzula acuminata	**wood-rush**	G	N	IR

❀   moist forests and forest openings; streambanks

Luzula acuminata

Luzula multiflora	**wood-rush**	G	N	IR

Isle Royale; rocky woods and openings

T   *Luzula parviflora*   **wood rush**   G   N   IR

Isle Royale only Michigan population; moist woods and gravelly lakeshores

►*Cyperaceae*   Sedge Family

Carex adusta	**sedge**	G	N	

dry open meadows

Carex aquatilis	**sedge**	G	N	IR

❀   wide variety of wetlands; shallow water

SC   *Carex arcta*   **sedge**   G   N

uncommon sedge of wet open places

Carex arctata	**sedge**	G	N	IR

moist, rich deciduous forests; less often under conifers

Carex argyrantha	**sedge**	G	N	IR

swamps; also sandy aspen woods; wooded dunes

T   *Carex atratiformis*   **sedge**   G   N   IR

rocky shoreline along Lake Superior; more common northward

Carex aurea	**sedge**	G	N	IR

❀   swamps, fens, wet places; sac around seed golden color

Carex backii	**sedge**	G	N	

dry, sandy or rocky meadows and woods

Carex bebbii	**sedge**	G	N	IR

❀   very common; wet places, open swamps, marshes, streambanks

Carex brevior	**sedge**	G	N	IR

dry, open sandy or rocky woods and meadows

Carex bromoides	**sedge**	G	N	

wet forests and wetland margins

Carex brunnescens	**sedge**	G	N	IR

swamps and wet forests; fens, beaver ponds

Status codes: *E* (endangered in Michigan), *T* (threatened in Michigan), *X* (extirpated from state), *SC* (special concern), *C2* (federal listing may be warranted but more information needed), *3C* (species once proposed for Federal listing but more abundant than previously believed).

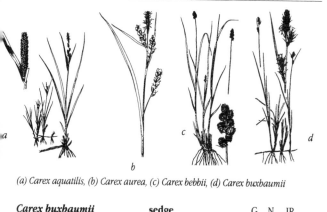

(a) Carex aquatilis, (b) Carex aurea, (c) Carex bebbii, (d) Carex buxbaumii

Carex buxbaumii   sedge   G N   IR
❀   may form large stands in marshes and wet meadows; rocky
    shoreline of Lake Superior

Carex canescens   sedge   G N   IR
    wet places; rocky shoreline

Carex capillaris   sedge   G N   IR
    swamps and moist forests, wet openings; rock shoreline

Carex castanea   sedge   G N   IR
    moist conifer forests and swamps; Lake Superior rocky
    shoreline

Carex chordorrhiza   sedge   G N   IR
    rhizomatous sedge of sphagnum peatlands; sometimes in
    shallow water

Carex communis   sedge   G N   IR
    deciduous forests; sometimes mixed forests

Carex conoidea   sedge   G N
    moist openings and meadows; uncommon in U.P.

Carex crawei   sedge   G N
❀   moist or wet sand dunes; calcium-rich wetlands and swamps

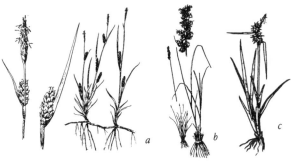

(a) Carex crawei, (b) Carex diandra, (c) Carex flava

Carex crawfordii   sedge   G N   IR
    wet sandy shores and openings; wooded dunes

Carex crinita   sedge   G N   IR
    swamps and marshes

Carex cristatella   sedge   G N   IR
    swamps and wet woods; Lake Superior rocky shore

Carex cryptolepis   sedge   G N   IR
    common in swamps and wet meadows; sandy wet areas

C Carex davisii   sedge   G N
    moist floodplain forests

Carex debilis   sedge   G N
    moist hardwood forests

Carex deflexa **sedge** G N IR
 moist openings in conifer or mixed forest; swamp margins

Carex deweyana **sedge** G N IR
 moist to dry deciduous or mixed forests

Carex diandra **sedge** G N IR
❀ swamps, marshes, and other wet places

Carex dioica **sedge** G N
 sphagnum peatlands; swamp openings

Carex disperma **sedge** G N IR
 sphagnum peatlands; cedar swamps; occasional in moist forests

Carex eburnea **sedge** G N IR
 wet cedar stands; gravelly or rocky shore along Lake Superior;
 may form dense carpets

Carex echinata **star-sedge** G N IR
 fens and swamps; shallow water

Carex exilis **sedge** G N IR
 fens and conifer swamps

Carex flava **sedge** G N IR
❀ sphagnum peatlands and swamps; marshes

Carex foenea **sedge** G N IR
 rock shore pools; dry jack pine woods and meadows

Carex folliculata **sedge** G N IR
 cedar swamps and fens

Carex gracilescens **sedge** G N
 rich deciduous and mixed forests

Carex gracillima **sedge** G N IR
 moist forests and conifer swamps; rocky shores

Carex granularis **sedge** G N
 wet places, swamps, moist woods, rocky shores

Carex gynandra **sedge** G N
 wet openings, streambanks

Carex boughtoniana **sedge** G N IR
 wet openings to dry rocky woods (Brockway Mountain) and
 dunes; disturbed areas

Carex bystericina **sedge** G N IR
❀ common wetland sedge in all but sphagnum; rocky shorelines

(a) *Carex bystericina,* (b) *Carex intumescens,* (c) *Carex lacustris,*
(d) *Carex lasiocarpa,* (e) *Carex oligosperma*

Carex interior **sedge** G N IR
 common in wet areas; swamps and fens; shallow water

Carex intumescens **sedge** G N IR
❀ low places in forests, conifer swamps, streambanks; spiklets
 large and inflated

Carex lacustris **sedge** G N IR
❀ shallow water, marshes, streambanks, swamps; often forming
 large colonies

Carex lasiocarpa   **slender sedge**   G N IR
❀   fens and floating mats; swamps

Carex lenticularis   **sedge**   G N IR
wet sandy or rocky shores along Lake Superior; marshy areas

Carex leptalea   **sedge**   G N IR
open peatlands, swamps, and wet meadows

Carex leptonervia   **sedge**   G N IR
deciduous forests, swamps, and fens

Carex limosa   **mud sedge**   G N IR
open peatlands and shallow pools

Carex livida   **sedge**   G N IR
floating mats, usually with sphagnum

Carex michauxiana   **sedge**   G N IR
wet hollows in dunes, ponds, fens and swamps

Carex norvegica   **sedge**   G N IR
rocky Lake Superior shore, rocky woods; in Michigan only
known from Isle Royale and Keweenaw Peninsula

Carex oligosperma   **sedge**   G N IR
❀   common in peatlands; strongly rhizomatous

Carex pallescens   **sedge**   G N
variety of moist habitats, both open and wooded

Carex pauciflora   **sedge**   G N IR
❀   common, distinctive sedge of open sphagnum mats

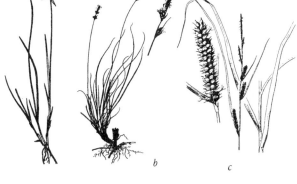

(a) Carex pauciflora, (b) Carex pensylvanica, (c) Carex rostrata

Carex paupercula   **sedge**   G N IR
fens and swamps; Lake Superior rocky shoreline

Carex peckii   **sedge**   G N IR
mixed forests; sometimes in swamps

Carex pedunculata   **sedge**   G N IR
deciduous and mixed forests; hummocks in swamps; early
fruiting habit, plants with red bases

Carex pensylvanica   **sedge**   G N
❀   dry, sandy jack pine or oak woods; dunes

Carex praegracilis   **sedge**   G N
western species rare in Michigan; known from wet hollows in
dunes near Eagle Harbor

Carex praticola   **sedge**   G N
moist woods; only collected once in Michigan in Houghton County;
more common to north and west

Carex projecta   **sedge**   G N IR
shallow water of swamps and beaver ponds; wet meadows

Carex pseudocyperus   **sedge**   G N
marshes, pond edges, peatlands; sometimes in shallow water

	Carex retrorsa	sedge	G	N	IR

swamps and ponds, hollows; often partly shaded places

SC *Carex richardsonii*   sedge   G   N

gravelly summit of Brockway Mountain

Carex rosea   sedge   G   N

rich deciduous or mixed forests

T   *Carex rossii*   sedge   G   N

in Michigan, known only from rock summits and Lake Superior shoreline of Keweenaw County

Carex rostrata   sedge   G   N   IR

❀   peatlands, shallow water, muddy areas; strongly rhizomatous; better referred to as *Carex utriculata*

Carex scabrata   sedge   G   N

in hollows and near springs in rich deciduous forests

T   *Carex scirpoidea*   sedge   G   N

rocky shores near Eagle River; uncommon in Michigan

Carex scoparia   sedge   G   N

moist, open places; wetland margins

Carex sprengelii   sedge   G   N

moist forests and meadows

SC *Carex squarrosa*   sedge   G   N

uncommon sedge of swamps

Carex sterilis   sedge   G   N

peatlands; elsewhere in U.P. in low, often marly spots between dunes near Lake Michigan

Carex stipata   sedge   G   N   IR

❀   common sedge of all wetlands except sphagnum peatlands

(a) Carex stipata, (b) Carex vesicaria, (c) Dulichium arundinaceum

Carex stricta   sedge   G   N   IR

shallow water, pond margins, marshes

Carex tenuiflora   sedge   G   N   IR

uncommon; peatlands

Carex tetanica   sedge   G   N

wetlands; uncommon in U.P.

Carex tribuloides   sedge   G   N   IR

wetlands

Carex trisperma   sedge   G   N   IR

usually in conifer swamps

Carex tuckermanii   sedge   G   N

wet woods and forest hollows; not in sphagnum peatlands

Carex umbellata   sedge   G   N   IR

sandy or gravelly places, rocky shores

Carex vaginata   sedge   G   N   IR

mossy swamps; species more common northward

Carex vesicaria   sedge   G   N   IR

❀   common sedge of marshy areas, beaver ponds, pond margins

Status codes: *E* (endangered in Michigan), *T* (threatened in Michigan), *X* (extirpated from state), *SC* (special concern), *C2* (federal listing may be warranted but more information needed), *3C* (species once proposed for Federal listing but more abundant than previously believed).

Carex viridula   **sedge**   G N IR
  wet, sandy to rocky shores and pools

Carex vulpinoidea **sedge**   G N
  wet open areas; lake margins, streambanks

Cladium mariscoides **twig-rush**   G N IR
  floating mats; wet shores

Cyperus esculentus **yellow nutgrass** G N
  open marshy areas; sometimes on disturbed ground

Dulichium arundinaceum **three-way sedge** G N IR
 ❀ peatland mats, marshes and shallow water; often forming
   large patches

(a) Eleocharis palustris, (b) Eriophorum polystachion, (c) Eriophorum vaginatum,
(d) Rhynchospora alba

Eleocharis acicularis **spike-rush**   G N IR
  wet sandy or muddy shores; small plants only several inches tall

Eleocharis flavescens **spike-rush**   G N
  muddy or sandy pond shores

Eleocharis ovata   **blunt spike-rush** G N IR
  muddy lakeshores

Eleocharis palustris **spike-rush**   G N IR
 ❀ wetlands, marshy shores; alkaline soil

Eleocharis pauciflora **spike-rush**   G N IR
  wet sandy shores and flats; sometimes in peatlands

Eleocharis robbinsii **spike-rush**   G N
  sandy or peaty pond and lake margins

Eleocharis tenuis   **northern spike-rush** G N IR
  wet, sandy or rocky lake edges and beaches

Eriophorum gracile **slender cotton-grass** G N IR
  sphagnum peatlands

Eriophorum polystachion **thin-scale cotton-grass** G N
 ❀ sphagnum peatlands, open marshes

Eriophorum tenellum **conifer cotton-grass** G N IR
  swamps and open peatlands

Eriophorum vaginatum **tussock cotton-grass** G N IR
 ❀ large clumpy plants of fens and tamarack and black spruce
   swamps; also called *Eriophorum spissum*

Eriophorum virginicum **tawny cotton-grass** G N
  common in conifer swamps and fens

Eriophorum viridicarinatum **dark-scale c.-grass** G N IR
  open fens and swamps

Rhynchospora alba   **beak-rush**   G N IR
 ❀ open conifer swamps and fens

Rhynchospora capillacea **beak-rush**   G N
  wet sandy or gravelly shores and marshes; wet places in dunes

---

feform codes: *T* (tree), *S* (shrub), *H* (herbaceous flowering plants), *G* (grasses and grass-like
lants), *F* (ferns and fern-allies). Origin codes: *N* (native to Upper Peninsula), *I* (introduced species).
resent on Isle Royale: *IR* (present), *blank* (absent). ❀ indicates an illustrated species.

Rhynchospora fusca   **beak-rush**   G   N   IR
     sandy shores and peatlands; low spots between dunes

Scirpus acutus   **hardstem-bulrush**   G   N   IR
     emergent along pond and lakeshores; may form large colonies

Scirpus americanus   **threesquare**   G   N
     sandy or gravelly lakeshores; strongly 3-angled stems

Scirpus atrovirens   **black bulrush**   G   N   IR
     wetlands

Scirpus cespitosus   **tufted bulrush**   G   N   IR
     peatlands and rocky crevices along Lake Superior; plants
     densely tufted

Scirpus cyperinus   **wool-grass**   G   N   IR
     ✿   common plant of marshes, swales, ditches, and open wetlands

Scirpus budsonianus   **bulrush**   G   N   IR
     peatlands; mature flowers with whitish bristles

Scirpus microcarpus   **bulrush**   G   N   IR
     moist, sandy shores along Lake Superior; pond margins

Scirpus pendulus   **bulrush**   G   N
     wetland openings and margins

Scirpus subterminalis   **water-bulrush**   G   N   IR
     shallow ponds and lakes; plants with floating leaves except for
     upright flowering stem

SC *Scirpus torreyi*   **Torrey-threesquare**   G   N
     wet sandy shores and shallow water

Scirpus validus   **softstem-bulrush**   G   N   IR
     ✿   wet shorelines and shallow water of ponds; may form large
     patches

a) Scirpus cyperinus, (b) Scirpus validus

▶ *Poaceae*   Grass Family

Agrostis capillaris   **Rhode Island bentgrass** G   I
     lawn grass; rarely escaped

Agrostis gigantea   **redtop**   G   I   IR
     ✿   common naturalized grass

Agrostis byemalis   **ticklegrass**   G   N   IR
     diversity of habitats including jack pine plains and other sandy
     or rocky areas

Agrostis perennans   **autumn bentgrass**   G   N
     moist to dry deciduous woods

Agrostis stolonifera   **creeping bentgrass**   G   N/I
     moist meadows and marshy places

Status codes: *E* (endangered in Michigan), *T* (threatened in Michigan), *X* (extirpated from state), *SC* (special concern), *C2* (federal listing may be warranted but more information needed), *3C* (species once proposed for Federal listing but more abundant than previously believed).

Alopecurus aequalis　　　　short-awn foxtail　　G　N
　　wet places; sometimes in shallow water

Ammophila breviligulata　　beach-grass　　　　　G　N
　❊　common colony-former on sand dunes along Great Lakes

Andropogon gerardii　　　　big bluestem　　　　G　N
　　jack pine plains, sand dunes and sandy fields

Anthoxanthum odoratum　　sweet vernal grass　　G　I
　　moist meadows and roadsides; sand dunes; annual Eurasian
　　grass

Aristida basiramea　　　　　forktip three-awn　　G　N
　　in Keweenaw, only collected once near Cliff Mine

Arrenatherum elatius　　　tall oatgrass　　　　G　I　　IR
　　Isle Royale; usually moist soil of clearings

Avena fatua　　　　　　　wild oats　　　　　G　I
　　waste places

Avena sativa　　　　　　　oats　　　　　　　G　I
　　waste areas; escape from cultivation

Beckmannia syzigachne　American sloughgrass　G　N　IR
　　Isle Royale; wetlands; rare in Michigan

Brachyelytrum erectum　　brachyelytrum　　　　G　N
　　rich deciduous forests

Bromus ciliatus　　　　　　fringed brome　　　　G　N　IR
　　forest hollows and wetlands

Bromus inermis　　　　　　smooth brome　　　　G　I　　IR
　　introduced pasture grass; meadows and roadsides

Bromus secalinus　　　　　cheatgrass　　　　　G　I
　　roadsides and waste places

Calamagrostis canadensis　blue-joint　　　　　G　N　IR
　❊　wet open places, common

Calamagrostis lacustris　　reedgrass　　　　　　G　N　IR
　　uncommon along rocky shores and ridges; similar to *C. stricta*

Calamagrostis stricta　　　reedgrass　　　　　　G　N　IR
　　rocky Lake Superior shoreline; sand dunes

Calamovilfa longifolia　　　prairie sand-reed　　G　N
　　sand dunes

Cinna latifolia　　　　　　drooping woodreed　　G　N　IR
　　wet places in forests; swamps

Cynosurus cristatus　　　　dogtail　　　　　　G　I　　IR
　　Isle Royale; dry openings

Dactylis glomerata　　　　orchard-grass　　　　G　I　　IR
　　naturalized pasture grass

C *Danthonia intermedia*　　timber-oatgrass　　　G　N
　　only Michigan collection from meadows near Cliff Mine

Danthonia spicata　　　　　poverty-oatgrass　　G　N　IR
　❊　dry sandy jack pine woods, dunes, rocky shores and ridges
　　increases after disturbance

(a) Agrostis gigantea, (b) Ammophila breviligulata, (c) Calamagrostis canadensis

eform codes: *T* (tree), *S* (shrub), *H* (herbaceous flowering plants), *G* (grasses and grass-like
ants), *F* (ferns and fern-allies). Origin codes: *N* (native to Upper Peninsula), *I* (introduced species).
esent on Isle Royale: *IR* (present), *blank* (absent). ❊ indicates an illustrated species.

98

*(a) Danthonia spicata, (b) Deschampsia cespitosa, (c) Elymus canadensis,
(d) Elytrigia dasystachya, (e) Glyceria canadensis, (f) Glyceria striata,
(g) Leersia oryzoides, (h) Oryzopsis asperifolia, (i) Panicum capillare,
(j) Panicum virgatum*

Deschampsia cespitosa   **tufted hairgrass**   G N IR
   ❀ rocky Lake Superior shoreline

Deschampsia flexuosa   **hairgrass**   G N IR
   dry jack pine woods; sand and rock ridges and dunes

Digitaria ischaemum   **smooth crab-grass**   G I
   dry roadsides and disturbed places

Echinochloa crusgalli   **barnyard-grass**   G I
   moist fields and roadsides

Echinochloa muricata   **barnyard-grass**   G N
   ditches and wet waste places

Elymus canadensis   **Canada wild rye**   G N
   ❀ dunes and thickets; roadsides

Elymus glaucus   **blue wild rye**   G N
   dunes, rocky woods and shorelines along Lake Superior

Elymus trachycaulus   **slender wheatgrass**   G N IR
   dry jack pine and oak woods; sand dunes

Elymus virginicus   **Virginia wild rye**   G N
   wet woods and swamps; streambanks

Elymus wiegandii   **broad-leaved wild-rye**   G N IR
   streambanks in woods

Elytrigia dasystachya   **thickspike wheatgrass**   G N
   ❀ sand dunes near Lake Superior; also known as *Agropyron dasystachyum*

Elytrigia repens   **quack-grass**   G I IR
   introduced grass of fields, gardens, and roadsides; also known as *Agropyron repens*

Elytrigia smithii   **western wheatgrass**   G N
   native sod-forming grass of western US; in Michigan mostly in disturbed places; also known as *Agropyron smithii*

Elytrigia spicata   **bluebunch wheatgrass**   G N
   in Michigan, collected once in 1895 on rocky bluffs of Keweenaw County; may be extinct from state; also known as *Agropyron spicatum*

Eragrostis cilianensis   **stink grass**   G I
   dry fields and waste places

Eragrostis tephrosanthos   **love grass**   G N
   uncommon on waste places, mine tailings

Festuca brachyphylla   **fescue**   G N IR
   dry pine and oak woods, sand dunes, rocky shores and ridges

Festuca elatior   **tall fescue**   G I
   fields and roadsides

Festuca occidentalis   **western fescue**   G N IR
   dry woods and wooded dunes

Festuca ovina   **sheep-fescue**   G I
   dry pine and oak woods; fields

Festuca pratensis   **meadow-fescue**   G I
   moist fields and disturbed places

Festuca rubra   **red fescue**   G N/I
   variety of open habitats

Glyceria borealis   **northern mannagrass**   G N IR
   shallow water and pond margins, marshes, ditches

Glyceria canadensis   **rattlesnake-mannagrass**   G N IR
   ❀ shallow water and marshes; peatlands

Glyceria grandis   **American mannagrass**   G N
   shallow water; streambanks, marshes, ditches

Glyceria striata   **fowl-mannagrass**   G N IR
   ❀ wetlands; most common mannagrass

---

ifeform codes: *T* (tree), *S* (shrub), *H* (herbaceous flowering plants), *G* (grasses and grass-like ants), *F* (ferns and fern-allies). Origin codes: *N* (native to Upper Peninsula), *I* (introduced species). esent on Isle Royale: *IR* (present), *blank* (absent). ❀ indicates an illustrated species.

Hierchloe odorata   **sweet grass**   G   N   IR
  sweet-smelling grass of moist meadows and wetlands

Hordeum jubatum   **foxtail-barley**   G   I   IR
  roadsides and waste places

Hordeum vulgare   **barley**   G   I
  cultivated barley; occasional escape but not persisting

Leersia oryzoides   **rice cut-grass**   G   N
  ❀ variety of wet places; may form a distinct band of vegetation

Lolium perenne   **ryegrass**   G   I
  pasture grass; escape to roadsides, yards, etc.

Lolium temulentum   **darnel**   G   I
  uncommon exotic of waste places; collected only twice in
  Michigan (once in Hancock)

Melica smithii   **awned melic grass**   G   N
  moist deciduous or mixed forests

Milium effusum   **milium**   G   N   IR
  moist deciduous or mixed forests; moist openings

X   *Muhlenbergia cuspidata*   **muhly**   G   N
  in Michigan, known only from 2 collections in Keweenaw
  County at Cliff Mine and Eagle Harbor

Muhlenbergia frondosa   **muhly**   G   N
  streambanks and wetland edges

Muhlenbergia glomerata   **marsh wild-timothy**   G   N   IR
  peatlands and marshy areas

Muhlenbergia mexicana   **muhly**   G   N
  swamps, fens, and marshes; moist hardwood forests

Muhlenbergia uniflora   **muhly**   G   N   IR
  wet shorelines and flats; rock pools

Nardus stricta   **moor-matgrass**   G   I
  introduced, densely tufted grass; old collections from several
  wet places in Houghton County

Oryzopsis asperifolia   **rough-leaved ricegrass**   G   N   IR
  ❀ sandy jack pine and oak woods and wooded dunes; deciduous
  and mixed forests

Oryzopsis pungens   **ricegrass**   G   N   IR
  dry, sandy jack pine or oak woods; wooded dunes; rocky ridges

Panicum boreale   **panic-grass**   G   N
  damp, sandy or rocky openings; sometimes in dry woodlands

Panicum capillare   **witch grass**   G   N
  ❀ disturbed openings and waste places; native but often weedy

Panicum columbianum   **panic-grass**   G   N
  dry sandy woods and dunes

Panicum depauperatum   **panic-grass**   G   N   IR
  dry sandy woods and wooded dunes; rocky ridges

Panicum dichotomiflorum   **panic-grass**   G   N
  moist fields and disturbed places; native but weedy

Panicum lanuginosum   **panic-grass**   G   N
  common in a wide range of habitats - wetland margins to dry,
  sandy woods and fields

Panicum leucothrix   **panic-grass**   G   N
  sandy woods and meadows

Panicum linearifolium   **panic-grass**   G   N
  wooded dunes; dry sandy jack pine or oak woods

Panicum miliaceum   **broomcorn millet**   G   I
  Old World plant, occasionally escaped

Panicum virgatum   **switch grass**   G   N
  ❀ dunes and sandy woodlands; roadsides

Status codes: *E* (endangered in Michigan), *T* (threatened in Michigan), *X* (extirpated from state), *SC* (special concern), *C2* (federal listing may be warranted but more information needed), *3C* (species once proposed for Federal listing but more abundant than previously believed).

Panicum xanthophysum   **panic-grass**   G N IR
    sandy jack pine, aspen, and oak woods; wooded dunes

Phalaris arundinacea   **reed canary-grass**   G N/I IR
✸   marshes, ditches and swales, streambanks; common and
    aggressive spreader

Phalaris canariensis   **canary-grass**   G I
    escape but not persisting; source of commercial bird seed

Phleum alpinum   **mountain-timothy**   G N
    in Michigan, only several old collections from Keweenaw
    County; may be absent from state

Phleum pratense   **timothy**   G I IR
    naturalized, spreading plant of fields and roadsides

Phragmites australis   **common reed**   G N IR
✸   marshes, swamps; often in standing water and forming large
    colonies

Poa alpina   **alpine bluegrass**   G N IR
    rock crevices along Lake Superior; rare in Michigan, more
    common northward to Arctic

Poa alsodes   **bluegrass**   G N IR
    rich hardwood or mixed forests

Poa annua   **annual bluegrass**   G I IR
    roadsides, lawns and disturbed places

Poa canbyi   **Canby's bluegrass**   G N IR
    rock crevices on shores of Isle Royale; plant rare in Michigan
    and more common in western US

Poa compressa   **Canada bluegrass**   G I IR
    introduced grass of old fields and roadsides; dry woods of jack
    pine, oak, or aspen

Poa glauca   **bluegrass**   G N IR
    rocky shorelines and ridges

Poa nemoralis   **bluegrass**   G N IR
    rocky shores; dry rocky openings

(a) *Phalaris arundinacea,* (b) *Phragmites australis,* (c) *Poa pratensis,*
(d) *Trisetum spicatum,* (e) *Zizania aquatica*

C2	**Poa paludigena**	**marsh-bluegrass**	G	I
/T	sphagnum peatlands; rare			
	Poa palustris	**fowl meadow grass**	G N?	IR

Poa palustris   **fowl meadow grass**   G N? IR
widespread in wetlands and moist areas; rock shores along Lake Superior

Poa pratensis   **Kentucky bluegrass**   G N/I IR
❀ common species of all but wettest habitats

Poa saltuensis   **bluegrass**   G N IR
forests, wooded dunes, rocky ridges

Puccinellia pallida   **puccinellia**   G N IR
streamsides, swamps and thickets

Schizachne purpurascens   **false medic**   G N IR
woods and openings; often on sandy or rocky soil; attractive purplish spikelets

Secale cereal   **rye**   G I
cultivated rye; sometimes an escape but not persisting

Setaria glauca   **yellow foxtail**   G I
introduced weedy grass from Europe

Setaria italica   **foxtail-millet**   G I
fields and waste places; grown as a grain by Indians

Setaria viridis   **green foxtail**   G I
introduced grass of roadsides, fields and disturbed places

Sphenopholis obtusata   **wedge-grass**   G N
dry woods and openings; uncommon

Sporobolus vaginiflorus   **dropseed**   G N
dry meadows and rocky areas; presence in Keweenaw based on doubtful collection

Trisetum melicoides   **trisetum**   G N
rocky or gravelly shores; cedar swamps

SC **Trisetum spicatum**   **trisetum**   G N IR
❀ rock shores and ridges

Triticum aestivum   **common wheat**   G I
cultivated; occasional, non-persistent escape

Zizania aquatica   **wild rice**   G N
❀ shallow, slightly flowing water of rivers, lakes and ponds; occurs both in wild stands and seeded as a crop

► *Sparganiaceae*   Bur-reed Family

Sparganium americanum   **bur-reed**   G N IR
shallow water of wetlands and shores; bur-reeds are important foods for waterfowl

Sparganium angustifolium   **bur-reed**   G N IR
shallow water

Sparganium chlorocarpum   **bur-reed**   G N IR
shallow water, shores and wetlands

Sparganium eurycarpum   **giant bur-reed**   G N IR
❀ shallow water, pond margins and wetlands; most common bur-reed; plants may be 3-4 feet tall; fruits round, bur-like clusters

Sparganium fluctuans   **bur-reed**   G N IR
shallow water of lakes and ponds

Sparganium minimum   **bur-reed**   G N IR
our smallest bur-reed; floating leaves in shallow water; shores

Status codes: *E* (endangered in Michigan), *T* (threatened in Michigan), *X* (extirpated from state), *SC* (special concern), *C2* (federal listing may be warranted but more information needed), *3C* (species once proposed for Federal listing but more abundant than previously believed).

Typhaceae   Cat-tail Family

Typha latifolia   **common cat-tail**   H N IR
  shallow water of marshes; no space on stem between male and
  female flowers; cat-tails important food for beaver and muskrat

Pontederiaceae   Water-hyacinth Family

Pontederia cordata   **pickerel-weed**   H N
  ❀ shallow water and marshy areas; showy violet flowers

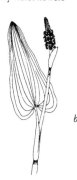

(a) Sarganium eurycarpum, (b) Pontederia cordata

Liliaceae   Lily Family

Allium schoenoprasum   **chives**   H N
  native chives, found on rock crevices and streambanks; rare
Asparagus officinalis   **garden asparagus**   H I
  cultivated escape; established in waste places
Clintonia borealis   **corn-lily, bluebead-lily** H N IR
  ❀ moist forests of all types; hummocks in swamps; dark blue
  berries
Convallaria majalis   **lily-of-the-valley**   H I
  ornamental; occasionally escaping or found around old
  homesteads
Erythronium albidum   **trout-lily**   H N
  in U.P. known only from Sturgeon River, Houghton County
Erythronium americanum   **trout-lily**   H N
  ❀ moist deciduous or mixed forests; forming colonies; flowers
  yellow; plants with pair of brown or purple mottled leaves
Hemerocallis fulva   **orange day-lily**   H I
  cultivated lily; occasional along roads
Lilium michiganense   **Michigan lily**   H N
  swamps, marshy areas, streambanks
Lilium philadelphicum   **wood-lily**   H N IR
  jack pine and aspen woods, dunes, sandy or rocky openings;
  flowers orange-red, opening upward
Maianthemum canadense   **wild lily-of-the-valley** H N IR
  ❀ ubiquitous in forests; also in peatlands and dunes
Muscari racemosum   **grape-hyacinth**   H I
  occasional garden escape
Polygonatum pubescens   **Solomon's seal**   H N IR
  hardwood forests; flowers green-yellow; fruit a dark blue berry

---

eform codes: *T* (tree), *S* (shrub), *H* (herbaceous flowering plants), *G* (grasses and grass-like
ints), *F* (ferns and fern-allies). Origin codes: *N* (native to Upper Peninsula), *I* (introduced species).
esent on Isle Royale: *IR* (present), *blank* (absent). ❀ indicates an illustrated species.

(a) Clintonia borealis, (b) Erythronium americanum, (c) Maianthemum canadense, (d) Smilacina racemosa, (e) Smilacina trifolia, (f) Streptopus amplexifolius (g) S. roseus, (h) Trillium grandiflorum, (i) Uvularia grandiflora

Status codes: *E* (endangered in Michigan), *T* (threatened in Michigan), *X* (extirpated from state), *SC* (special concern), *C2* (federal listing may be warranted but more information needed), *3C* (species once proposed for Federal listing but more abundant than previously believed).

Smilacina racemosa **false Solomon's seal** H N IR
- ✿ usually in moist hardwood forests; sometimes drier woods and wooded dunes; white flowers in terminal spike; fruit red with brown spots when ripe

Smilacina trifolia **false Solomon's seal** H N IR
- ✿ peatlands; berries at first brown-speckled, turning translucent red

Smilax ecirrata **carrion-flower** H N
moist hardwood or mixed forests; streambanks; plants not vining

Stenanthium gramineum **featherbells** H I
established in marshy area near M-28 along Houghton-Baraga county line

Streptopus amplexifolius **twisted stalk** H N IR
- ✿ hollows and seeps in moist forests; cedar swamps; stems smooth; flowers green-white; fruit red

Streptopus roseus **twisted-stalk** H N IR
- ✿ mixed forests and cedar swamps; stems hairy; flowers pink to purple; fruit a bright red berry

Tofieldia glutinosa **false asphodel** H N IR
rock crevices along Lake Superior; wet places between dunes

Tofieldia pusilla **false asphodel** H N IR
Isle Royale; wet rocks and pools along shoreline

Trillium cernuum **nodding trillium** H N IR
conifer swamps; wet birch woods; leaves three in a whorl, fruit a dark red berry

Trillium grandiflorum **big white trillium** H N IR
- ✿ moist forests; sometimes conifer swamps; single 3-parted white flower

Uvularia grandiflora **bellwort** H N IR
- ✿ moist hardwood forests and openings; plants with nodding yellow flowers before leaves fully open

Iridaceae Iris Family

Iris versicolor **northern blue flag** H N IR
- ✿ wetlands; plants to 3 feet high; flowers blue, one to several

Sisyrinchium angustifolium **blue-eyed-grass** H N
rocky openings, streambanks

Sisyrinchium montanum **blue-eyed-grass** H N IR
- ✿ grassy clearings, ditches, railroad grades

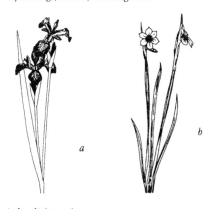

(a) Iris versicolor, (b) Sisyrinchium montanum

▶ *Orchidaceae*   Orchid Family

Aplectrum hyemale   **putty-root, Adam and Eve** H   N
❀   uncommon in Keweenaw in moist woods or swamps; flowers brown-purple with white, purple-spotted lip; single basal leaf

Arethusa bulbosa   **arethusa, dragon's mouth** H   N   IR
❀   usually on sphagnum; attractive plant of peatlands; flowers bright magenta-pink

Calopogon tuberosus   **grass-pink**   H   N   IR
❀   fens and swamp openings; flowers magenta-pink

T   *Calypso bulbosa*   **calypso, fairy slipper** H   N   IR
     shaded conifer woods on old beach ridges; moist, mostly conifer forests; uncommon

Corallorhiza maculata   **spotted coral-root**   H   N   IR
❀   dry to moist woods and wooded dunes

Corallorhiza striata   **striped coral-root**   H   N   IR
     cedar woods and swamps, mixed forests

Corallorhiza trifida   **northern coral-root**   H   N   IR
❀   cedar swamps; moist mixed forests; often in shade

Cypripedium acaule   **moccasin-flower, pink l.s.** H   N   IR
❀   wet conifer woods and swamps; moist mixed forest; our most common lady-slipper; plants single flowered on naked stalk; lip pink with crimson veins

3C/ *Cypripedium arietinum*   **ram's head l.-slipper**   H   N   IR
SC   moist, wooded sandy or rocky soils; conifer swamps; lip white with purple

Cypripedium calceolus   **yellow lady-slipper**   H   N   IR
❀   usually in wet woods and peatlands, often under cedar; lip yellow, often with purple veins

Cypripedium reginae   **showy lady-slipper**   H   N   IR
❀   shrubby peatlands and open cedar or tamarack swamps; lip pink with white furrows

Goodyera oblongifolia   **w. rattlesnake-plantain** H   N   IR
❀   moist to dry conifer forests

Goodyera pubescens   **downy rattlesnake-plantain** H   N
❀   mixed forests and conifer swamps; flowers green-white in dense terminal spike; rosette of dark green leaves with net-like white veins

Goodyera repens   **lesser rattlesnake-plantain** H   N   IR
     mixed woods and conifer swamps

Goodyera tesselata   **rattlesnake-plantain**   H   N   IR
❀   mixed forests and cedar swamps; moist places in dunes; often found with *Goodyera repens*

Habenaria clavellata   **club-spur orchid**   H   N   IR
❀   swamps and fens; plants with yellow-green flowers

Habenaria dilatata   **tall white bog-orchid**   H   N   IR
❀   cedar swamps (openings), fens

Habenaria hookeri   **Hooker's orchid**   H   N   IR
     mixed forests and wooded dunes

Habenaria hyperborea   **tall n. bog-orchid**   H   N   IR
     wet woods and cedar swamps

Habenaria lacera   **ragged fringed orchid** H   N
     swamps and fens

Habenaria obtusata   **blunt-leaf orchid**   H   N   IR
     conifer swamps and woods; fen margins

Habenaria orbiculata   **round-leaved orchid**   H   N   IR
     conifer swamps and moist mixed forests

Status codes: *E* (endangered in Michigan), *T* (threatened in Michigan), *X* (extirpated from state), *SC* (special concern), *C2* (federal listing may be warranted but more information needed), *3C* (species once proposed for Federal listing but more abundant than previously believed).

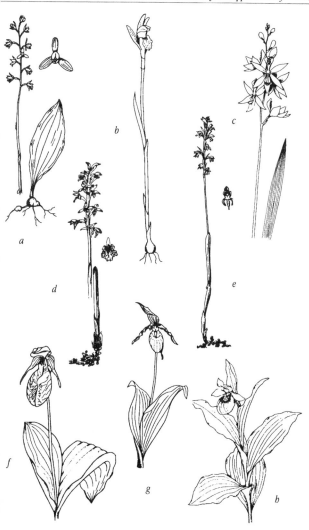

(a) *Aplectrum hyemale,* (b) *Arethusa bulbosa,* (c) *Calopogon tuberosus,*
(d) *Corallorhiza maculata,* (e) *Corallorhiza trifida,* (f) *Cypripedium acaule,*
(g) *Cypripedium calceolus,* (h) *Cypripedium reginae*

Habenaria psycodes   **purple fringed orchid** H N   IR
  ❀ open peatlands; rock ledges along Lake Superior; showy
     purplish or lavender flowers; lower lip 3-lobed and fringed
Habenaria viridis   **bracted orchid**   H N   IR
     mixed forests and wooded dunes
Liparis loeselii   **fen orchid**   H N   IR
  ❀ inconspicuous yellow-green orchid of peatlands
Listera auriculata   **auricled twayblade**   H N   IR
     conifer forests on Isle Royale
Listera convallarioides   **broad-leaved twayblade** H N   IR
  ❀ moist conifer forests and streambanks
Listera cordata   **heart-leaved twayblade** H N   IR
     swamps and fens
Malaxis monophyllos   **white adder's-mouth**   H N   IR
     hummocks in swamps, wooded dunes
Malaxis unifolia   **green adder's-mouth**   H N   IR
     rocky openings and swamps; sandy soil with bracken fern

Form codes: *T* (tree), *S* (shrub), *H* (herbaceous flowering plants), *G* (grasses and grass-like
plants), *F* (ferns and fern-allies). Origin codes: *N* (native to Upper Peninsula), *I* (introduced species).
Present on Isle Royale: *IR* (present), *blank* (absent). ❀ indicates an illustrated species.

E *Orchis rotundifolia* **one-leaf orchis** H N IR
   uncommon on Isle Royale; rare in Michigan, more common
   northward

Pogonia ophioglossoides **rose pogonia** H N IR
   ❀ sphagnum peatlands; flowers pale crimson-pink

Spiranthes casei **Case's ladies'-tresses** H N
   rocky ridges and outcrops; occasionally in old fields
   and roadsides; *Spiranthes* have white flowers

Spiranthes cernua **nodding ladies'-tresses** H N IR
   open moist places in forests; low spots in dunes

Spiranthes lacera **slender ladies'-tresses** H N IR
   ❀ dry jack pine woods and dunes; rocky soils

Spiranthes romanzoffiana **hooded ladies'-tresses** H N IR
   ❀ wet openings and roadside ditches; wet places between dunes;
   cedar swamps

*(a) Goodyera oblongifolia, (b) Goodyera pubescens, (c) Goodyera tesselata,
(d) Habenaria clavellata, (e) Habenaria dilatata, (f) Habenaria psycodes,
(g) Liparis loeselii, (h) Listera convallarioides, (i) Pogonia ophioglossoides,
(j) Spiranthes lacera, (k) Spiranthes romanzoffiana*

Status codes: *E* (endangered in Michigan), *T* (threatened in Michigan), *X* (extirpated from state),
SC (special concern), *C2* (federal listing may be warranted but more information needed), *3C*
(species once proposed for Federal listing but more abundant than previously believed).

Illustration Credits

Unless otherwise noted below, illustrations are reprinted from: *Flora of Alaska and Neighboring Territories: A Manual of the Vascular Plants* by Eric Hulten with the permission of the publishers, Stanford University Press. © 1968 by the Board of Trustees of the Leland Stanford Junior University.

Other illustrations are from the following sources and used with permission (number and letter refer to page number and figure).

Common Flowering Plants of the Northeast. Donald D. Cox. 1985. State University of New York Press, Albany. 32b; 33b; 35a; 35c; 42c; 43a; 44b; 45b; 52a; 55a; 56a; 63c; 66; 72b; 75b; 77d; 80a, b, d, f (top); 80b, e, f (bottom); 83c; 84a; 87b; 88a, c; 104a, b, c, h, i; 105b; 107a, b, f, g: 108b, d, e, f, k.

Ferns and Fern Allies of Canada. William J. Cody and Donald M. Britton. 1989. Agriculture Canada, Ottawa. Reproduced with the permission of the Minister of Supply and Services, Canada, 1996. 22e, h; 25a, b, c; 27a (top); 27b, c (bottom); 28c, e; 29b (top).

Forest Trees of Illinois. Robert H. Mohlenbrock (no date). Illinois Dept. of Conservation. 29b (bottom); 30a, b, c; 36; 37a; 67b, c..

Freshwater Wetlands: A Guide to Common Indicator Plants of the Northeast. Dennis W. Magee. The University of Massachusetts Press, Amherst. 31d; 36b; 57a (bottom); 64a, b; 74; 84g; 85a, c; 87a; 88d, e, f; 94c; 98g; 101a, e; 103b; 105a; 107c.

An Illustrated Flora of the Northern United States and Canada. Nathaniel Britton and Addison Brown. (2nd ed.). 1913. Charles Scribner's Sons, New York. 26a (top); 26a, b, c (bottom); 28b; 32a; 36a; 38; 39b; 42a, b; 44; 46c, d, e, f, g, h; 50d, e, f, g; 53c (bottom); 54a, b, c, d (bottom); 55a, b (top); 56b; 57a, c (top); 57b (bottom); 59; 59a, b; 60c; 62; 63b, c (bottom); 65b; 67; 67a, d; 68b, c, d; 78b, c, d, e; 84c, d, e, f; 108a, c, g.

A Manual of Aquatic Plants. Norman C. Fassett. 1940. The University of Wisconsin Press, Madison. 73; 92c, d, e.

Manual of the Grasses of the United States. A. S. Hitchcock and Agnes Chase. 1950. USDA Misc. Publication No. 200. 97a, b, c; 98b, c, d, e, f, h, i, j; 101b, e.

Michigan Wildflowers. Helen V. Smith. 1966. Cranbrook Institute of Science Bulletin 42 (a division of Cranbrook Educational Community). Cover; 107d, e; 108h, j.

New York Botanical Garden. *Sphagnum* illustration, page 10.

▶Index to Plant Families & Genera

DATE DUE

12-12-97